HAUNTED
LIVERPOOL
ANTHOLOGY

© Tom Slemen 2006

Published by The Bluecoat Press, Liverpool
Book design by March Graphic Design Studio, Liverpool
Printed by Ashford Colour Press

ISBN 1 904438 41 5

Tom Slemen

HAUNTED LIVERPOOL
ANTHOLOGY

The Bluecoat Press

CONTENTS

INTRODUCTION

The forty-seven stories in this book have been selected from the twelve volumes of my *Haunted Liverpool* series, and I hope these tales will provide those readers who are not familiar with my work with a good impression of what my writing is all about. One of the commonest questions I am asked relates to the source of my stories. They are derived from the general public and my research. Every year I receive hundreds of emails, letters and phone calls from people who have strange stories to tell, and I also scour the Liverpool newspaper archives in the local history department of the Central Library on William Brown Street. Of course, not every story that is related to me, or uncovered in the archives, will make it into print, usually because there is little substance in some of the tales, and I am very particular about those I use. A single cubic mile of seawater contains, on average, twenty tons of gold, but to get that gold we would need filtration techniques presently undreamt of. The ratio is similar to the large volume of stories I wade through each year; only a small percentage are gold standard and will find their way into one of my books.

Some of the stories within this anthology have given me sleepless nights over the years. When I was a child, living on Myrtle Street, I often lay in bed at night thinking about 'Spring-Heeled Jack' – the Victorian bogeyman who could make amazing leaps from pavement to rooftop, who had been seen by many credible witnesses, including the Duke of Wellington, and my grandmother's mother! I was worried that he might still be around. When I was a kid, I looked upon my grandmother, Rose Slemen, born in the 1890s, as a surviving Victorian. She told me endless stories about ghosts, old Lancashire folklore and gruesome tales of crime. She never lied, not once, and was much respected for her honesty – she was a very straight-talking woman, and so, when she casually brought up the subject of Spring-Heeled Jack one evening, she caught my attention immediately. She told me how her own mother had seen him jumping off a rooftop near St Francis Xavier's Church, and how everyone thought he was the Devil himself visiting Everton. One night I was staying at my Gran's home when I woke to find a strange shadowy face peering at me through the living room window – and we were on the second floor! I immediately assumed that it was Spring-Heeled Jack, but it turned out to be just a burglar on a ladder, much to my disappointment!

Classic unsolved mysteries have also given me insomnia on many occasions. Sometimes the human mind just cannot give in and concede that there are certain things we will never know. For example, what happened to Lord Lucan? Who really shot President Kennedy? And what happened to the crew of the *Mary Celeste*? This latter mystery has continued to puzzle people since 1872. The two-masted sailing ship set out from New York harbour on a trip to Genoa carrying a cargo of whale oil and 1,701 barrels of commercial alcohol. The ship was later found adrift near the Azores – minus the captain, his wife and child, and all of the crew – and none of these people was ever seen again. To add to the mystery, there was six months' supply of food and water onboard, and all of the crew's tobacco and personal belongings had been left behind, as if they had all deserted the ship in a great hurry. The vessel was found to be completely seaworthy and not in any danger of sinking, so why had everyone left her in such great haste? I believe I have finally solved this world-famous mystery, but you'll have to read *Haunted Liverpool 10* to read my solution. The many legends and claims surrounding the disappearance of the crew of the *Mary Celeste* have been included in this book as a taster to the world's greatest maritime mystery.

Do such creatures as vampires really exist? Two vampires feature in this book: the Lodge Lane Vampire and Mr Sphinx, and both of these tales document incidents that actually happened. A man is entombed, and three days later, in the wee small hours, escapes from his sealed up tomb. I believe that Jesus performed such a resurrection thousands of years ago – but have lesser mortals, or even immortals, ever carried out such an incredible feat? Some believe vampiric beings still exist today; that they leave their graves after nightfall and set off in search of blood, and sometimes 'prana'; the life-energy of the living. I once interviewed three unrelated people who lived near the Earle Road area of the city, who all had strange puncture marks on their necks. Each had awakened at around 3am and found their pillows damp with blood, and had then gone to the doctor when the puncture marks started to bleed again, hours after the blood had clotted. Skin infections were ruled out, as the marks were too localised and deep. One wound – in the neck of a seventeen-year-old girl – took almost a fortnight to fade. The doctor was baffled by the strange marks and joked to himself that Dracula was at large – but this was around the time of the Lodge Lane vampire scare.

On Sunday, 16 April 1922, a man was walking down Coventry Street, in London's West End, when something invisible bit into his neck. The man felt blood being rapidly drawn from his neck and he passed out. He was taken to Charing Cross Hospital, and when he regained consciousness, a surgeon told him that he had been stabbed in the neck by some kind of thin tube which had siphoned off a quantity of blood. The victim said he had seen no such attacker with a tube. He was soon discharged from hospital – and two and a half hours later, another man was admitted with the very same type of puncture mark in his neck. It transpired that he too had been walking down Coventry Street when he had felt an intense pain in his neck, followed by the sensation of blood being sucked out of his body. He had then passed out. Later that evening a third victim of the invisible bloodsucker was brought into Charing Cross Hospital, and yes, like the two previous victims, this man had also been attacked at the same spot on Coventry Street. The surgeon wasn't prepared to stick his neck out (no pun intended), to say who, or what, he thought the bloodsucker of Coventry Street might be, as it was 1922, and he was in the modern metropolis of London and not some Transylvanian village in the eighteenth century. But, he must have harboured dark suspicions about the unearthly attacker.

I have always been fascinated by the nature of time, and long before I read the theories of Einstein, Lobachevsky and Riemann, I knew that the events of the past were still going on somewhere along the timeline – they were just out of reach of the normal five human senses. Man seems to be the only animal troubled by time. We have built megalithic monuments such as Stonehenge, which seem to be some sort of stone-age clock and calendar, aligned to the sun, stars and moon. We have striven to invent ingenious calendar systems to divide time into years, months, weeks and days, and we have even devised ultra-accurate atomic clocks that have split a second into a 'femtosecond' – or one billionth of one millionth of a second. We have taken a razor blade to a second and shaved it down to a femtosecond, but this still doesn't answer the age-old question: what is time? Our grammatical structures are devised in such a way that we are able to pinpoint exactly when an action happened by the use of past and future tenses, and we all know about hours, minutes and seconds, but what is actually being referred to when we picture time?

The philosopher Immanuel Kant believed newborn babies had a sense of the passage of time. If this was so, it would mean that time is all in the mind; that it is, in fact, a sixth sense. As you read this book now, do you have a rough idea of what time it is without looking at the clock? You probably aren't far out in your estimation, but if you were trapped down a mine, without a clock or watch, you'd find that your perception of time was way out of sync with the actual time. Trapped miners stranded for twenty-four hours below ground have imagined themselves to be trapped for days. Time therefore, is largely a construct of the human mind. Our bodies age of course, but you may notice how some people age at a quicker rate than others, because ageing is a genetic process, and has little to do with the passing of the years. When we speak of time, we usually mean clock time, which was invented to make sense of the order of events in our lives, but a clock has little to do with time.

Is time travel possible? I once asked my science teacher at school if it would be possible for me to move through time into the future, and he laughed and said it wasn't possible, as time travel was impossible. I told him that I was already moving through time into the future, along with him and the rest of the class at a rate of sixty seconds per minute – he told me to be quiet and to get on with my course-work.

The most famous time-travel novel has to be *The Time Machine* by HG Wells. Published in 1895, it was a unique tale, as its hero deliberately set off for unknown destinations in the realms of time – in an actual machine. Since then, the Wellsian idea of time travel has been borrowed and stolen by many science fiction writers. However, is time travel really possible? Well, many physicists have drawn up the equations, and time travel does seem to be a real possibility, but it seems just beyond the grasp of modern science at the moment. If time travel will one day be a reality for us, could we be getting visited by time-travellers now? Well, there are some strange people who have turned up in our history books, who seem to have been time-travellers.

A curious individual who called himself the Count of St Germain, arrived out of the blue on the European scene in 1710. He appeared to be about forty-five to fifty years of age, and was seen by the composer Jean-Phillippe Rameau and the young Countess von Georgy in Venice. From 1737-1742, the Count was at the court of the Shah of Persia, where he showed an extensive knowledge of diamond creation and repair, way ahead of its time. The year 1743 found the mysterious Count at the court of King Louis XV, where he gave demonstrations of diamond-enlarging and talked about Cleopatra, Jesus Christ and other historical personages as if he had personally known them. In 1745 he turned up in London and was arrested as a suspected Jacobite sympathiser. The writer Horace Walpole, who interrogated the man of mystery said, "He sings and plays on the violin wonderfully, composes, is mad and not very sensible." The Count was released after questioning, and was then accepted into the glittering aristocratic society of the Viennese court, where he lived as a prince. He was next seen in India by Sir Robert Clive, and the Count hinted that he was a traveller in time.

Between 1757 and 1760, the Count of St Germain was at the height of his fame in the court of Louis XV, and he met Countess von Georgy – who was now in her seventies, yet she noticed that the Count still looked as if he were between forty-five and fifty years of age – he had not changed since she had met him as a little girl in Venice. Upon the death of the King of France, the Count warned the new monarch, King Louis XVI and Marie Antoinette about 'a gigantic conspiracy' that would overthrow the order of things. No one listened, and when the French Revolution arrived, the Count had long fled the country. However, he is said to have appeared to Marie Antoinette as a comforting vision when she ascended the scaffold to be beheaded. The Count faked his death on several occasions, but was still spotted, usually dabbling in politics, for many years afterwards. They say the Count never died, and he himself claimed that he had travelled through both space and time.

In this book you will find the strange case of the 'Timewarp Chippy' – a long-demolished building from the 1960s which reappeared one night at the location where it once stood, only to vanish again after being visited by two students. Such timewarp incidents fascinate me, and lead me to believe that a crossing of the time-barrier might eventually be smoother and easier than crossing the sound-barrier.

Of course, the main theme of this book is Liverpool and the ghosts who inhabit this great city. I once dated a very sceptical girl who repeatedly told me that I was wasting my time collecting these 'silly' ghost stories. However, one day, in the 1990s, my girlfriend and I were in a very famous store on Liverpool's Church Street, when she put her hand to the back of her neck and looked around. I asked what was the matter and she said that someone had just squirted water at her. The back of her dress was drenched and yet there was no one else on that floor, only two women at the tills at the far side. My girlfriend mentioned the strange incident to the woman at the till, and she was told that a ghost they had nicknamed 'Lulu' had haunted the store for years, and she always squirted water at people's backs for some odd reason. Sometimes her ghostly giggling was heard, but she was rarely seen. Those who had seen her said she was dressed in the style of the 1930s. I went to the spot where the water had been squirted and could still see the water on the floor. I looked up at the ceiling, thinking a leak or a faulty fire sprinkler might be to blame, but could see nothing to confirm my suspicions. My girlfriend found the whole incident deeply disturbing and never set foot in that store again.

I have studied Liverpool's ghosts for years, and I do not doubt their existence. Are they the spirits of the deceased, or are they something more sinister or demonic? Some manifest themselves as rather shy apparitions and others as vicious and destructive poltergeists. I believe that most people who die go on to the place where they feel they belong, a sort of 'going home' ritual, but sometimes people can't, or don't want to leave their loved ones behind. Others may have become so attached to a place where they worked, or lived, that they choose to hang around in spirit form as a ghost.

For those of you who scoff at the idea of phantoms, may I remind you that you may become a ghost yourself one day?

TOM SLEMEN

ROLL OUT THE BARREL

It is all in the mind, sceptics often declare, when somebody reports a ghost, but the psychological explanation simply does not apply when a paranormal incident is experienced by more than one person. Undoubtedly, some ghosts are all in the mind, I do not deny that. Floorboards, mice and pipes can create noises which can generate phantasms in the human imagination, especially in the middle of the night. However, when a ghost is actually observed by multiple witnesses, all rational explanations must go out of the window. The following phantom was observed by several people over a prolonged period of time and its presence is backed up with the historical facts relating to the ghost.

Up in Blundellsands there stands an old Victorian house which overlooks the waters of Liverpool Bay. In the 1950s, a gang of workmen was charged with the task of converting the waterfront house into flats. Before the workmen started their job, the foreman started a full inspection of the run-down property. In the attic, he stumbled across something highly unusual: the huge helm wheel of an old ship, that had been mounted in front of the garret window. The bemused foreman surmised that the previous occupant must have been either a sailor or a sea captain and, as he playfully turned the wheel, he looked beyond the dusty attic window at the sea's horizon.

Meanwhile, one of the workers was examining an array of maps and charts that dotted the wall. These maps covered every part of the globe. More maritime items were uncovered in the attic that afternoon: a sextant, a finely-balanced compass, a small brass folding telescope and a huge, battered-looking trunk. The foreman fully expected the trunk to be locked but when the lid was lifted open it revealed nothing but an old sword, which resembled an eighteenth century naval cutlass. He carefully lifted the sword out of the trunk and, as he did so, he and the labourer were startled by the sound of an accordion playing somewhere in the house, accompanied by the cries of seagulls. As the foreman turned to the workman with a look of puzzlement, he noticed that the old ship's wheel had started spinning on its axis. The workman turned and witnessed this strange activity too, upon which he started to back out of the attic, muttering, "I don't like this one bit, I'm off!"

The foreman was more amazed than frightened, that is until events took an even stranger turn. Another weird noise reverberated throughout the attic, just like the creaking of a ship's timbers. Suddenly, the entire floor seemed to tilt and sway and the two men feared that the whole building was ready to collapse. With the helm spinning and the yells of the phantom seagulls, the foreman felt as if he was standing on the swaying deck of a ship at sea. He decided to run but, as he bolted for the door, something powerful yanked the old sword from out of his hand. He glanced backwards and saw the cutlass suspended in mid-air, as if hanging by an invisible thread.

Understandably, the foreman and his gang refused to work in the attic and instead of converting it into a room, they left it the way it was and simply locked the door. When the landlord of the old house heard this, he took the foreman to court. All the same, even he did not like the spooky atmosphere in the attic and never ventured up there alone. He knew that, in the 1860s, a demented sea captain named William Stewart lived in the Blundellsands house, and, according to old rumours, he had been a cruel and twisted man, who had committed some unspeakable act of evil on the premises. No one knew just what Captain Stewart was supposed to have done, but the landlord had heard from his father that there had been a double murder in the house long ago.

In 1955, the Blundellsands dwelling was sub-divided into six flats, which were occupied by five couples and an elderly spinster. In April 1955, the spinster, Jean Fleming, let out a scream one night at half past twelve. Two medical students and their girlfriends, who were lodging at the house, ran up to the third floor flat to find out what was the matter. They discovered Miss Fleming lying on the floor, unconscious. When she came to, she claimed she had fainted after seeing a terrible apparition. The bodies of a naked man and woman were lying on her bed, dismembered and disembowelled. Their heads, arms and legs had been severed from their torsos and it had all looked so real, she had even seen the blood soaking into her duvet. She was so terrified that she left the lodging house that night and went to stay with a cousin in Kirkdale. Everyone in the lodging house surmised that the confused old lady had simply had a bad dream. But, later that week, in the dead of night, something took place which turned all the lodgers into shambling nervous wrecks.

The time was 3.15am and a young couple on the ground floor were awakened by a loud bang which echoed down the stairway. It seemed to originate in the attic. They listened intently and heard a succession of thumps on the stairs. Then the strains of an accordion playing some sort of sea shanty drifted down the stairway.

On the second floor, the medical students and their girlfriends were also awakened by the racket and one of the girls got out of bed and looked through the keyhole. She let out a terrible scream, then rushed into the arms of her alarmed boyfriend, who was sitting up in bed. "What's wrong? Who is it?" he asked. She hugged him and started to shake violently. She claimed that a weird-looking man, with wild staring eyes was on the landing outside, trying to carry a barrel down the stairs. The man wore a leather cap and a long black coat and he had blood on his hands.

The two students were so frightened that they refused to budge from the room until first light and barricaded themselves in behind the door. Across the landing, the other medical student, a young man named Robert, had made the mistake of opening the door to find out who was making all the noise. He got the clearest view of the strange man, before slamming the door and locking it. He later described the man as outdated, with a black cap similar to the ones worn by the sea skippers in the nineteenth century. Robert had seen the bloody hands too and had also noticed blood around the man's mouth, on his grizzled beard and in his moustache. The odd-looking stranger's glaring mad eyes had also sent a shiver down his spine.

The couple in the ground floor flat did not dare to open their door to see what all the commotion was about, but they noted how the rumbling sound and strange music seemed to continue down into the cellar, where it came to an abrupt end.

The lodgers soon realised that a ghost was at large in the house and contacted the landlord to tell him about the nerve-shattering episode. He visited the house and instead of dismissing the claims, he seemed very jumpy and on edge. When he went up to the attic, he found that the door had been forced open. He arranged for a new padlock to be fitted to the door but, in the following week, the sinister man in black gave a repeat performance, only this time, the terrified lodgers who were brave enough to peep through their keyholes, saw that the seafaring shade was now pulling a trunk down the stairs. On this occasion, he was heard to cackle and mutter to himself in a raspy voice as he made his way down to the cellar.

Enough was enough and early next morning there was nothing short of a mass exodus from the haunted lodging house. The landlord begged them to stay but soon found himself alone in the house. As a last resort, a priest was invited in, to exorcise the ghost but even he fled when he allegedly saw the blade of the old sword being thrust at him through the attic door. As the priest and the landlord flew down the stairs in a state of absolute panic, the sound of laughter reverberated through the house. The landlord later died after a short illness and the house was bought by a wealthy retired couple from Aintree named Joan and Freddie Osborne.

A few days after the Osbornes had moved in, they, too, heard the spooky sea shanty being played somewhere in the building by an invisible accordion. Then, in June 1958, Joan Osborne awoke in bed one night to be confronted by the menacing ghost of the bearded sea captain leaning over her. His wide, insane-looking eyes peered into her terrified face and she was paralysed with fear. The ghost's face was spattered with droplets of blood. He raised his arm, brandishing a long sword in his hand, ready to strike her. She managed to squeeze her eyes closed and, suddenly regaining the power to move, let out a scream, thinking some burglar was about to slay her in her bed. Her husband bolted upright from the bed and he actually watched as the ghostly sea captain melted away into the darkness of the bedroom.

The Osbornes got in touch with a local historian friend, named Ian MacCauley, who specialised in maritime history. They asked him to research the history of their newly-purchased house and, over the next two months, he uncovered a disturbing tale of murder and madness which seemed to explain the ghostly phenomena. He learned that, in the 1860s, a Captain William Stewart had bought the property. Stewart had a streak of insanity which he had undoubtedly inherited from his grandfather, a captain who had murdered seven of his own crew on a ship called the Mary Russell in 1828. Stewart's grandfather had stood trial for murder and had been found guilty and insane. After serving seven years at an asylum in Cork, he had been released to return to his hometown of Liverpool.

Like his grandfather, William Stewart was also accused of murdering one of the crewmen on a ship named the Seabird, in 1859, but he was later acquitted. After a prosperous career importing rum and sugar from Barbados, Captain Stewart retired and married an Irish girl by the name of Mary O'Monoghan. The couple moved into the waterfront house at Blundellsands and when Stewart learned that his old ship, was being decommissioned, he salvaged the wheel of the vessel, along with several sections of the deck. The floorboards of the deck were laid in the attic of their new home and the helm was also mounted in front of the attic window. The ship's sextant and compass were also recovered by Stewart for sentimental reasons and he kept them in a trunk, along with his trusty old spyglass and sword.

Stewart's neighbours nicknamed him 'Jack Tar' and often sneered at the way the old seafarer went down to the waterfront promenade each morning to feed the seagulls. But what really amused his neighbours, was the way he stood before his attic window, manipulating the wheel of his ridiculous, imaginary ship, as he gazed out at the distant horizon of Liverpool Bay.

Then Mary Stewart went missing. People asked William what had become of her but the old seadog would only smile enigmatically and say, "Gone back across the Irish Sea no doubt". When Mary had not been seen in over a month, the neighbours alerted the police and the retired captain was taken into custody and quizzed. A thorough search of the house revealed bloodstains on the mattress of the Stewarts' double bed. Traces of blood were also found in a barrel and trunk in the cellar. When Stewart was asked to explain the bloodstains, he gradually became more and more incoherent and started to sing and laugh out loud.

He was committed to an asylum for the criminally insane and, in 1870, just before he died, he made a startling deathbed confession. He claimed that he had murdered his wife and her lover upon discovering them in his bed. On the night in question, a thunderstorm was raging, and Stewart was able to enter his house without being heard. In a fit of jealous rage, he entered the bedroom, then impaled Mary and her lover with his old sword, in one swift thrust through the man's lower back. He then hacked the screaming couple to death, dismembering their limbs in the process.

Stewart was so enraged at the man who had been to bed with his beloved wife, that he sliced off his ears and fried them in a pan before eating them. Stewart hid the gruesome body parts in a barrel and trunk that he kept in his attic, but later transferred the containers downstairs to the cellar. The arms, legs, torsos and heads were gradually sawn up into small chunks and fed to the seagulls during his morning walks along the promenades of Blundellsands and the fragmented bones of the murder victims were simply tossed into the sea.

When the Osbornes had heard the full story of the murderous Captain Stewart, they promptly abandoned their new home and put it up for sale. The house is still standing today and, for some reason, it lies empty!

The Sad Spectre of Smithdown Road

The following spooky incident happened in Liverpool in the early 1990s and was even reported in the *Liverpool Echo*. One morning, at around four o'clock, a twenty-four year-old man named Alan was walking home from a pub on Smithdown Road. There had been a stay-behind at the pub because the landlady was celebrating her recent engagement, and Alan felt quite drunk. He was walking near Sefton General Hospital, which is situated in Smithdown Road, when he noticed a girl standing on the pavement near a bus stop. She wore an incredibly short dress with a revealing top and had long blonde hair. She looked about nineteen or twenty and Alan assumed she was waiting for a taxi. She just stood there shivering, stamping her high heels on the pavement because of the cold.

"You're not on the game are you, love?" Alan joked, hoping to chat her up.

The girl smiled and shook her head.

"I'm freezing," she complained. "Why on earth did I come out without a coat?"

Alan saw his opportunity and quickly took off his denim jacket and offered it to her.

"Who said chivalry was dead?" he laughed, as the girl gratefully took the coat and put it on. It was at least three sizes too large and looked ridiculous on her and they both laughed.

"Waiting for a taxi?" Alan asked.

"No. Waiting for my boyfriend," she replied, looking down Smithdown Road for any sign of him.

Alan's heart sank.

"Just my luck," he thought. "She's already going out with someone."

"He does my head in, you know; I've been waiting here for ages. He always does this," added the girl.

"Does what?"

"Says he's gonna pick me up and then doesn't turn up."

"Get another boyfriend who's more reliable then," Alan said, giving her the hint.

"Nah, I can't do that. I love Tony," she answered, smiling dreamily.

"But does he love you?" asked Alan cheekily.

"Oh, I suppose he's not coming," said the girl, looking worried. "I wonder if something's happened to him?"

"No, he's probably with some girl. We fellas are only human y'know, despite our alien appearance," laughed Alan, trying to cheer her up.

The girl tutted and walked along. Alan walked along beside her, and couldn't help admiring her long legs and beautiful figure. She was a real stunner.

"What's your name?" he asked.

"Jodie."

"Ooh, Jodie Foster, eh? My name's Alan. My mates call me Alan Ladd."

Jodie smiled and walked on. Then she suddenly bowed her head as if she was going to cry and ran off into Toxteth Park Cemetery.

Alan surmised that she was either going to be sick because she had been drinking too much, or that she was going to 'powder her nose'. He wanted to relieve himself too, after all that drinking.

After about ten minutes, Alan shouted into the darkness of the cemetery.

"Jodie! Jodie! Are you okay?"

As he crept past the gravestones overgrown with grass and weeds, he could see no sign of her. He half expected to find her lying on the ground, out cold with drink, although she hadn't appeared to be in the least bit drunk. By now it was almost dawn and the sky was getting paler by the minute.

"You had me worried there, girl," he called out aloud as he thought he saw her, but it was only his denim jacket, draped over one of the gravestones. "What's she playing at?" he mumbled to himself.

As he removed his jacket from the gravestone, he saw Jodie's face on the stone – or a photograph of her to be precise – and, underneath the oval photograph, an inscription which stated that she had been born in 1970 and had died tragically in 1990, just six months earlier. Alan grabbed his jacket, and with feet like lead and legs like jelly, he stumbled out of the cemetery and back on to Smithdown Road. He did not stop running until he reached his home almost a mile away, where he fell down on his doorstep and with a trembling hand inserted the key into the Yale lock.

A week later, he told his two best friends about the ghost he had tried to chat up and Brian, one of his mates, recalled that his sister had been a friend of the dead girl. Brian then told the sad story of her death. Jodie had arranged to meet her boyfriend near the bus stop at Sefton General Hospital on Smithdown Road. She had not been aware that she had a hole in her heart which had been ticking inside her like a timebomb since she was a baby. That night she collapsed without warning on to the pavement and although people tried to help her by calling for an ambulance, there was nothing that anyone could do, and she died that night at the hospital. Shocked and bewildered, Jodie's parents telephoned her boyfriend and told him the terrible news, he was so devastated that he vowed never to drive up Smithdown Road again. To this day, he refuses to go anywhere near the road.

On the following night, Alan and Brian visited Jodie's grave and placed a bouquet of carnations on it because Brian's sister had told them that carnations had been her favourite flowers. As the lads walked away from the cemetery, Alan glanced back and was certain that he saw Jodie waving. The ghost of the dead girl is still occasionally seen by motorists driving up Smithdown Road in the early hours of the morning. As recently as 1996, a taxi driver stopped to pick up the girl at three in the morning, but when he looked around, the pavement was deserted.

THE RETURN OF WALTER SLIM

A former student of the University of Liverpool rang me one afternoon at the studios of Radio Merseyside to relate a story I had heard something of before. I often hear several versions of an alleged supernatural event, and more often than not, I have to try and 'iron out' the inconsistencies of the varying accounts to avoid contradictions arising. The following story, however, was related to me over a period of almost three years, from no fewer than seven people, and all of their recollections regarding a very strange tale concurred entirely. The last piece of the jigsaw which made the story complete was the discovery of a name in a Liverpool cemetery which I happened to stumble upon. Without further ado, here is the eerie tale of Walter Slim.

On the evening of Friday, 13 August 1971, at around nine o'clock, five male students left their lodgings on Liverpool's Upper Stanhope Street and headed for the Philharmonic pub on Hope Street. This was the so-called 'glam rock' era, with bands like T Rex appearing in the pop charts, and it wasn't unusual for the youth of the early seventies, especially students, to dress outlandishly. Two of the five students wore battered old top hats and Army trench-coats, and one even wore a deerstalker which sported a scarlet carnation. Fashion-wise, it was an era of anything goes.

The strangely-clad students decided to take a short cut through St James's cemetery next to the Anglican Cathedral, which is a creepy place even in broad daylight, but this was nine o'clock at night, and twilight heightened the supernatural menace of the vast graveyard. The students were glad when they had emerged unscathed on the other side of the cemetery, and they hurried past the Liverpool Institute (which is now the Fame School, LIPA).

At this point, one of the students, Douggie, noticed a stranger walking alongside them, wearing a top hat and a long black opera cloak. He also wore a white starched collar and a large bow tie. He was about six feet in height, and looked about thirty years old. His face was extremely pallid and anaemic-looking. Douggie nudged one of his friends, grimaced and asked, "Who's he?"

His friend looked at the stranger and shrugged. The students crossed Hardman Street, but the stranger stood rooted to the kerb, gazing in fascination at the cars waiting at the traffic lights. Douggie and his friends went into the spacious lounge of the Philharmonic pub, which was packed on this Friday night. Then, as Douggie was ordering a drink, he saw the top-hatted man in the cloak dash into the pub, throw back his cloak and screech with laughter. He looked as if he was demented, or possibly high on drugs. Everyone in the pub noticed the stranger and they all agreed that he was decidedly creepy. The barman looked him up and down and asked him what he wanted to drink, and in a strange-sounding voice the man said: "In the name of human charity, I'll have your gin, sir!"

The barman enquired how he wanted the gin, and the man in the topper impatiently waved his hand and shouted, "Gin, sir! Nothing else!" and he slapped the counter three times with the palm of his hand. Everyone backed off, because there was something extremely sinister about the man. A lot of people later recalled how he had given off an awful body odour, mingled with a sickly sweet scent, reminiscent of violets. The glass of gin was duly poured and placed before the eccentric stranger, and the barman held out his hand, expecting to be paid, but the stranger ignored him, swigging down the neat, undiluted gin and banging the glass down on the counter.

He then turned around and walked to a corner where a black girl was standing on her own. The girl was exceptionally beautiful and wore her hair in the popular 'Afro' style. She backed up against the wall as the malodorous man approached. He grabbed her hand, kissed her knuckle, and simultaneously tilted his hat. "My name is Walter Slim," he said, and his dark eyes seemed to smile, though his lips did not move. He asked the girl her name.

"Sarah," she said, very self-consciously.

"What a delightful name!" Walter chimed, and began to ramble on about how his father had supported the campaign to end the despicable institution of slavery. He then lapsed into sentimentality, and in a choked-up voice, he said, "Many, many years ago, I loved a girl named Sarah. The beautiful Miss Sarah Beaton."

Walter then produced a beautiful silver locket and opened it to show Sarah the oval portrait within of a young golden-haired lady. Tears rolled down Walter's face as he described how Sarah had died from a fever, just days before he was due to marry her. She had been just seventeen. The twentieth century Sarah felt great sympathy for the smelly stranger, and subconsciously realised that he must be some sort of flesh and blood ghost. For some reason she was no longer afraid.

"I feel quite ill," Walter said suddenly.

At this point, the barman who had been diddled out of his money, told him to get out, saying that he was permanently barred. Walter stumbled out of the pub into the night, with Sarah following him. Her friends begged her not to go after him, because he was obviously mad, but she ignored them and set off after him. She followed him to the cemetery nestling in the shadow of the Gothic splendour of the massive sandstone Anglican Cathedral, and she immediately noticed how he seemed terrified of the traffic plying its way along Rodney Street. Sarah squinted into the darkness and watched him stagger into the blackness until he could no longer be seen. She was afraid of the dark at the best of times and wisely decided against going into the cemetery alone.

Well, that should have been that. The incident went down in Liverpool folklore; the far-fetched tale of Walter Slim, the Victorian ghost who called in for a gin at the Philharmonic pub, had even reached my young ears when I was a child living off nearby Myrtle Street. Some thought the visitation was a hoax, staged by some madcap student with a dark sense of humour on that Friday the thirteenth.

Then, one evening in July 2002, I was in the Everyman Bistro when I happened to meet a man named Ken, who had once been a photographer for the Liverpool Echo many years before. We chatted on the subject of the paranormal, and Ken mentioned that he had once been called out to take a photograph of a huge, eight-pointed, occult symbol, which black magicians had drawn in the cellar of the derelict John Bagot Hospital in the north of the city. The dabblers in the Black Arts had drawn up the symbol in the old hospital, because so many people had died there over the years, and the occultists probably wanted to try and channel the energy that had been released at that location to open up a portal to demonic entities.

Ken later produced the actual photograph. I had seen the strange symbols in the photograph somewhere before. I checked them against a photograph I had in my possession of an identical eight-pointed star scrawled in the desecrated tomb of a Victorian gentleman in the Cathedral cemetery off Hope Street in 1971. When I checked the name on this tomb, I saw that it read: 'Walter Slim, 1861-1888'. He had died at the tender age of twenty-seven. I then remembered the old tale about the ghost walking into the Philharmonic pub. The other name mentioned had been a Sarah Beaton. I also located her grave in the same cemetery. She had died in 1885, aged seventeen.

The occultists who had broken into Walter Slim's tomb had carried out one of the most controversial and terrifying rituals in black magic, the 'Octagenesis of Resurrection', which is purported to be a way of raising the dead. However, the revived corpse usually disintegrates after an hour or so. Only perfectly preserved corpses, taken from a lead-lined coffin, are used in the ritual. Walter Slim was laid to rest in just such a lead coffin.

DEADLY SECRET AT THE STINGO

HAUNTED LIVERPOOL 11

The following story was told to me several years ago, and, upon first hearing it, I was very dubious about its authenticity, until I researched the tale. I contacted people who were involved in the strange story, and soon came to realise that something sinister took place in 1960s Liverpool which defies explanation.

In 1961, a thirty-four-year-old man named Harry Turnbull was working for Martindale's Coal Merchants, and one November afternoon, after Harry had delivered coal to various houses on High Park Street, Toxteth, he and his friend Davy Rankin went for a couple of swift halves of bitter at a local public house called the Old Stingo. As the men warmed themselves by the blazing coal fire in the parlour, a knowledgeable pensioner was annoying the coal porters with a rather gloomy prediction. Ted Bunbury, aged seventy-four, held up a small lump of smouldering coal which he had picked up from the fire with a pair of tongs, and said: "Coal is prehistoric, and in a few years no house or factory shall use this stuff; nuclear power will take over."

"Oh put a sock in it," Harry muttered, leaning on the counter in the parlour, trying to block out the old prophet's predictions.

"Pity you won't be around to see all this come to pass, Ted," Davy Rankin cruelly remarked to the old freethinker.

Ted Bunbury threw the coal back into the flames, laid the tongs down beside the cast-iron fire surround, and then he approached the two coal men. He picked up Harry Turnbull's half-pint glass of bitter from the counter and said: "If all of the liquid in this glass could be converted directly into energy, it would produce an amount equivalent to the muscular energy expended in an entire day by the world's population. If we could convert half a pint of liquid entirely into energy we could produce enough power to propel a spaceship the size of St Paul's Cathedral to the nearest star."

Harry snatched the beer glass out the old man's hand. "I wish you'd propel yourself out of here, you old fool." he said to old Ted's stunned face.

As Ted went back to his usual corner seat of the pub in a huff, Harry Turnbull spotted a beautiful-looking girl of about seventeen or eighteen years of age, sitting at a table near the window. Although the girl looked half his age, Harry started to talk to her, and saw she was drinking sarsaparilla. He bought her a glass of Sarsaparilla and brought his own drink to her table. The girl gave her name as Cathy, and she looked beautiful, big large brown eyes, long black hair, and a fresh-complexioned face. Davy Ranking tried to talk his friend out of chatting up the girl because of her age, but Harry told him to mind his own business. Just over thirty minutes later, Harry and Davy were due back on the coal wagon, and before they left, Harry asked Cathy to meet him again at the pub. The girl said she would call in at noon on Saturday. On the day of the first date, Cathy was dressed in the height of fashion, and upon her head she wore a pillbox hat made from beaver fur fabric to defy the winter. Harry also looked suave in his well-cut Peter Pell tailored suit. The couple had a drink, then Harry took Cathy to Webb's Used Car Dealers in Berry Street. He had been looking at a cream 1959 Ford Zodiac for a few weeks now, and had decided to finally purchase it for £565.

Harry and Cathy cruised out of Liverpool in the Zodiac and ended up in a small cosy pub near Widnes. Harry sat with his arm around Cathy in an arched alcove at this old fashioned pub as they talked. They told one another about their lives, and one thing they had in common was a longing to find that elusive someone who could give them love and security. Harry felt as if Cathy was the type of girl he had been waiting for, for so many years. She got up to go to the toilet, and Harry smiled as she was gone. He decided he would jokingly tell her that he missed her when she returned, but Cathy didn't return. The minutes wore on, and there was still no sign of the girl. Harry ended up asking women emerging from the ladies' toilets if there was a girl of Cathy's description in there. They told him there was no one of Cathy's description in the toilet, and Harry was so puzzled and confused by the girl's disappearance, he barged into the toilets and had a look for himself. The pub landlord seized the coal-man's arm and asked him what his game was. Harry told him he couldn't find the girl he had come to the pub with, but the landlord told him he had seen no such girl. Harry pointed to the table in the alcove of the pub where he had been spending an intimate evening with Cathy and saw that the glasses she had sipped her drinks from had vanished, yet his own beer glasses, empty and full, were still there. Harry remembered the cigarettes Cathy had smoked while in his company, but all the cigarette butts in the ashtray had no lipstick traces. Harry drove round the area, looking for Cathy, and at one point beeped his horn at a girl on the road who wore a beaver fur pillbox hat, but when the young lady turned around, Harry was disappointed to see it was not his sweetheart.

Eventually Harry gave up and drove back to Liverpool. He recalled Cathy saying she had lived somewhere on Elaine Street in Toxteth, and so Harry called at every house on that short street, but no one had heard of Cathy. Harry even went to a police station and told them what had happened, but they told him there was nothing they could do if the missing girl's surname wasn't even known. For weeks, Harry frequented the Old Stingo pub where he had first set eyes on Cathy, in the hope he would see her again, but he never did. Davy told his friend that perhaps the girl had decided to leave him for some reason, and tried to console Harry by saying other girls would come along. Sure enough, on December 31 of that year, New Years Eve at around 7pm, Harry and Davy were in another Toxteth pub known as Poets Corner, on Park Hill Road, when a beautiful blonde woman of about thirty years of age walked into the premises. Male heads turned in the pub when the lady entered, and she went straight to the bar to order a drink. Harry stood there, agape, overawed by her stunning looks and shapely figure. Davy nudged him with his elbow to break the spell, and whispered: "Go on, what you waiting for?"

Harry sidled up to the beauty and saw her put a cigarette in her mouth. She searched her handbag for a lighter, and Harry dipped his hand in his coat pocket and withdrew a lighter in one swift movement. He flicked the cap off, thumbed it, and held the naked flame to the tip of the woman's cigarette. She inhaled, the tip of the cigarette glowed, and she turned to shoot a sensual smile at Harry. The world seemed to stop turning in that moment. Harry had never seen a female as beautiful as the woman standing before him. She sat on a bar stool, and after thanking the coal man for the light, she asked Harry what his name was. Harry told her, and she said he had the most interesting eyes she'd ever seen. It wasn't long before the two of them were chatting and drinking, and Davy Rankin also met a girl at the pub that evening named Anna. Anna, who lived on Marsh Lane, Bootle, was drinking with relatives from Park Road, and although she was nowhere as beautiful as the woman Harry was drinking with, she had a great sense of humour and a bubbly personality. The blonde Harry had met was named Simone White, and lived in the Dingle. She was single, and had recently broke off an engagement because her fiancee had cheated on her. Almost five hours passed by in that pub until the clock approached midnight. Soon 1961 would be gone forever, and people were pouring out of the pub on to the chilly street outside, where they got ready to hold hands in a circle to sing Auld Lang Syne. Everyone waited as the hour hand crept to twelve, and suddenly in the hush, there came the sounds of the foghorns on the river, and the distant cheers of people across the neighbourhoods. Simone held Harry's hand and they linked up with the circle of revellers outside. Davy Rankin held hands with Anna, and also joined the circle. Everyone started to move in a clockwise direction and someone started to sing:

Should auld acquaintance be forgot,
And never brought to mind?

The circle revolved, and Harry found himself singing as he looked up at the stars. All that drink and the intoxicating perfume of Simone made those stars swim about in the sky as he shuffled along in the circle, and when the song was done, he gazed sideways to the lovely Simone and found she had gone. Instead, Harry Turnbull's hand was clasping the hand of an old woman. He looked about confused, then released the old woman's hand. He broke up a passionate kiss Davy and Anna were enjoying, and asked his friend where Simone was. "How the Hell should I know?" was Davy's indignant reply. Harry searched the pub but the blonde was nowhere to be seen. He walked the streets of the area, looking for Simone, but it was as if she had vanished off the face of the earth, just as Cathy had done weeks before.

Harry awoke the following morning on a sofa at Davy's house, and in the first minute of waking it felt as if Simone and her mysterious disappearance had been some strange dream. As he struggled with the throbbing hangover, Harry asked Davy if he remembered Simone, and his friend said she was hard to forget, given the figure and face she had. Harry told him about the way she had vanished, just like Cathy had, and in reply, Davy had joked "You're cursed mate."

Harry returned to the Poets Corner pub and made enquiries about Simone, but no one knew anything about her. In desperation, Harry drove round the Dingle area, hoping to set eyes on the elusive blonde, but he never set eyes on her again. Deep down, Harry felt as if there was something sinister, almost supernatural about the two vanishing women. Harry was just a simple man, a coalman, yet he felt something – some higher intelligence – had been playing with him. It was hard to put into words. Davy Rankin certainly didn't know what he was getting at, but old Ted Bunbury, the intelligent man he had sneered at, might understand, Harry reasoned. He regretted mocking the intelligent old man who talked about coal becoming superseded by nuclear power, and wondered if he could throw any light on the mysterious disappearances of Cathy and Simone. Harry found the pensioner sitting on his own in the Old Stingo pub one quiet Sunday evening, and he bought Ted a drink. He told him what had happened in detail, then asked him if he could provide an explanation. The old man stared into the glass of stout, deep in contemplation, and after a tense pause he said, "Shakespeare said there are more things in Heaven and Earth than were dreamed of in our philosophy. Have you ever heard that quote?"

Harry shook his head.

"Well, let me put it this way son; the universe is a big place. Ever looked up at the stars at night?"

"Yes," Harry thought about that New Year night, when he saw the stars whirl about in a drunken lovelorn haze.

Mr Bunbury sipped the tangy stout, smacked his lips, then reflected on the scale of the cosmos. "Those stars are distant suns believe it or not, like the sun we have in our sky down here, and all those billions of suns out there have planets around them, and only God Himself, knows what beings live on those worlds. There might be beings out there who learned how to split the atom when the dinosaurs were still walking our world. They might be so advanced, they would regard us as either pests or playthings."

"I don't see what you're getting at," Harry admitted.

"Think of a rat in a maze," said the old man. "Behaviourologists study rats in mazes and note the way they react to certain stimuli to fathom out how their minds' tick. And for all we know, something up there might regard us as rats in a maze, and they might toy with our lives, and play tricks on our minds, just to see how we react. Maybe that's why people see flying saucers and ghosts. Maybe some sort of mind manipulation experiment is going on."

"You're so wise," Harry told the old man with great sincerity. "I'm sorry for the way I talked to you in the past; it's all down to my ignorance."

The man appreciated the apology and offered to get Harry a drink, but the coal man refused. Davy and Anna came into the pub, and Harry went to sit with them.

"Were you drinking with Mr Brain's Trust then Harry?" Davy asked, smirking at old Ted.

Harry said nothing, and asked Anna what she'd like to drink.

Almost an hour passed, and then Ted Bunbury came over to table where Harry Turnbull was sitting with Davy and Anna. The old man looked as if he had something very important to tell Harry.

"I've just worked out what's going on Harry, and it's incredible," said Ted, excitedly. Harry's attention was instantly engaged.

"Hey, beat it old man," Davy told the pensioner, but Harry gestured for his friend to shut up and rose from the table, highly intrigued.

"You won't believe what those girls were," Ted looked wild-eyed, as if he had uncovered some great yet dangerous secret. The old man trembled and his bottom lip quivered. He had Harry's undivided attention now.

"What?" Harry waited for the answer.

Something invisible seemed to strike the old man in the back, winding him, and sending the bottom set of his dentures flying on to the table where Davy and Anna were seated. Mr Bunbury's eyes turned upwards until they were white, and he started to fall. Harry caught him, then cradled the old man in his arms. He didn't know what to do, and as Anna screamed, blood came trickling down Ted's nose, as a faint dribble at first, then as an alarming red gush which turned the old man's shirt scarlet. The barman came rushing over, and he felt Ted's neck for a carotid pulse, but found none. An ambulance was called for, and Ted Bunbury was pronounced dead at the hospital. The pensioner had suffered a massive cerebral haemorrhage after a blood vessel had burst in his brain. Death had been instantaneous.

Harry Turnbull didn't accept the official mundane explanation for the old man's sudden death. Something had struck Mr Bunbury and sent his dentures flying out with the impact. Davy Rankin and Anna, as well as a handful of other drinkers at the pub had seen and heard the effects of whatever it was that struck the old man. Harry was left with the terrifying impression that Ted had been struck down by something because he had been about to reveal some terrible secret connected with the girls who had come into his life so transiently. Of course, it could all be a coincidence, and perhaps the girls simply left Harry for reasons known only to themselves, and he was merely unable to trace them. Harry however, thought differently, and believed Ted Bunbury had used his intellect to unravel some great mystery that should have been left well alone; a dangerous secret which cost him his life.

PLOUGHBOY PROPHET

The word prophet usually conjures up visions of bearded biblical characters from the Old Testament, but in more recent times there have been secular-minded individuals who have had the talent (some might say handicap) of seeing into the future.

One such seer was the Cheshire Prophet, an uneducated ploughboy of the fifteenth century, named Robert Nixon. Robert was born in 1467, the only son of a virtually destitute Cheshire farmer. Farmer Nixon had long since resigned himself to the fact that his mentally disabled son would never amount to anything in life, so he had put him to use in the field as a ploughboy. The unfortunate lad was frequently scoffed at by the locals and labelled the village idiot because of the apparent slowness of his mind. His appearance also made him an object of ridicule as his head was unusually large and he had huge, protruding eyes. Despite all the spiteful jibes to which he was subjected, the ploughboy was thoroughly good-natured and inoffensive and rarely said anything to anyone beyond a simple "yes" or "no".

One day, out of the blue, Robert suddenly surprised everyone, by predicting that an ox belonging to a neighbouring farmer would die. Not long after he had uttered the prediction, he and a group of curious villagers watched helplessly as the healthy-looking ox in the next field collapsed. When the beast was examined, minutes later, it was found to have died from no apparent cause.

News of the uncanny prophesy reached the ears of local aristocrat, Lord Cholmondeley, who sent for Robert and kept him at his estate for a short while. The country squire tried to encourage the boy to learn to read and write, but Robert resisted all attempts to be educated, so he eventually left the estate and ended up back at the handles of his father's plough.

A couple of days after leaving Lord Cholmondeley's estate, Robert was ploughing one of his father's fields, when he suddenly stopped mid-furrow and stared skywards with gaping mouth. The farm overseer ordered him to get on with his work, but the ploughboy remained rooted to the spot, engrossed in something which he could obviously see in the clear blue sky. The overseer struck Robert with a strap and told him to stop daydreaming, but the boy was oblivious, even to the strap, and did not react.

For the space of an hour, the ploughboy stood gazing up at something in the heavens, which no one else could detect, until he finally broke out of his trance-like state and resumed his ploughing as if nothing had happened. The overseer was burning with curiosity and urged the lad to reveal what he had been staring at. Robert thought about it for a while and then replied enigmatically, "I have seen things that I cannot tell you and which man never saw before".

This unusually loquacious answer shook the overseer, who was used to the boy's monosyllabic utterances. Not only that, the ploughboy's voice had assumed a new clarity and speed of delivery, so unlike his usual muffled speech. It was almost as if something, or someone, was using the boy as a mouthpiece. There were to be further strange vocal deliveries from the farmer's son.

One day, before a group of startled drinkers in the local tavern, Robert held forth for two hours, in the accentless voice of his mysterious alter ego, expounding his theories about the "history of the future". This unbelievably comprehensive lecture included details about the rise of an individual named Oliver Cromwell, the Civil War, the subsequent beheading of Charles I, the Restoration of the Monarchy, the reign of William of Orange and the French Revolution. Towards the end of his epic discourse, Robert predicted the abdication of James II in 1688:

"When a raven shall build its nest in a stone lion's mouth on top of a church in Cheshire, a King of England shall be driven out of his kingdom to return nevermore. As token of the truth of this, a wall of Mr Cholmondeley's shall fall!"

Lord Cholmondeley heard of the prediction and laughed it to scorn. He examined the wall mentioned in the ploughboy's prediction and, finding it to be completely secure, he assured his bailiff that young Robert would be wrong on this occasion. The bailiff laughed and nodded in agreement. However, the very next day the apparently structurally-sound wall inexplicably crumbled to the ground. The remainder of Robert's prediction came true centuries later, when a raven did indeed build its nest in the mouth of a stone lion gargoyle at the top of a Cheshire church in 1688 – a mere day before King James II was deposed. The dethroned monarch later died in exile at Saint Germain in France.

On 22 August 1485, the Cheshire Prophet (as Robert Nixon had now come to be known) was ploughing a field, when once again he angered his overseer by stopping abruptly in his tracks. Before he could administer his usual swipe with the strap, Robert suddenly lifted his whip and started brandishing it about, as if it were a sword.

"There, Richard! There!" he shouted. "Now! Up, Henry! Up with all arms! Over the ditch, Henry! Over the ditch and the battle is won!"

An excited gaggle of farmworkers came rushing across the field and eagerly gathered around Robert, who was now standing inert, with a mysterious smile on his face. Then he suddenly raised his whip in the air and declared, "The battle is over! Henry has won!"

The farmworkers fell about laughing at the ploughboy's ludicrous amateur dramatics. But these same peasants became curious two days later, when two travel-weary messengers rode into the county of Cheshire with important news – King Richard III had died at Bosworth while fighting the Earl of Richmond, now King Henry VII of England. When one of the villagers asked the messengers the exact date on which King Richard had died, he was told that he had met his death on 22 August, the same date on which the Cheshire Prophet had given his performance of the remote battle, by simultaneously enacting the event at Bosworth.

On the day that the messengers arrived with the news of King Henry's victory, the ploughboy became extremely agitated and nervously asked several of the villagers if he could take refuge in their homes.

"Why? Who are you hiding from, Robert?" asked one bemused villager.

"The king's men, of course!" he replied, "They're coming for me. They want to take me to the royal palace and if I go there, I'll be sure to die of thirst and starvation!"

The villagers could make no sense of the ploughboy's babblings. For what possible reason would the King want anything to do with the village idiot? And, for that matter, how would a guest starve in a royal palace?"

A few days later, several of the King's men rode to the Nixon farmstead looking for the famous Cheshire Prophet. When they caught up with Robert, they escorted him to King Henry, who was fascinated by the tales he had heard of the idiot-genius who could foresee the future.

The King assigned a scribe to accompany the ploughboy at all times, and to record any predictions he should enunciate. One of the first prophecies to be recorded by the scribe concerned a future event that apparently has not yet happened. Nixon prophesied that soldiers, with white dust on their helmets, would invade the country through a tunnel.

Before setting out on a fortnight-long hunting trip, the King left instructions with his cooks to give the Cheshire Prophet all the food he desired. The cooks initially obeyed the king's commands but, after a few days, they tired of the ploughboy's incessant greed and decided to lock him up in a heavy oaken chest, until he was really hungry, just to teach him a lesson. In the hustle and bustle of palace life, the cooks completely forgot about the tiresome ploughboy until, two weeks later, when the King returned and asked if the Cheshire Prophet had made any more predictions whilst he had been away. Only then did the cooks remember that they had locked him up. With great trepidation, they rushed to the thick-timbered chest and opened it to find that Robert Nixon had died from thirst and starvation.

The Cheshire Prophet's prediction of his own tragic death had come to pass.

DEAD MAN WALKING

HAUNTED LIVERPOOL 8

To preserve confidential details, the names of the persons mentioned in the following story have been changed. Arrad Street is an L-shaped back-street that runs from Hope Street to Oxford Street, passing behind a row of houses and the Everyman Theatre. Today it is a lonely, dimly-lit street, but in the 1950s it was even darker, with just a solitary lamp on Oxford Street to illuminate one end of the narrow, cobbled passageway.

At this location in the April of 1956, Arrad Street was the backdrop to a very uncanny event. Before I relate the strange proceedings that took place there, I must go back further in time to the autumn of 1955.

On a November evening of that year, there was an electrifying boxing match at Liverpool Stadium. Liverpool's own middleweight, Billy Ellaway, dazzled the crowds with his onslaught against Guyana-born Kit Pompey. In the audience, a man and a woman sat in their ringside seats, holding hands as they watched the journeymen pugilists engaged in combat. Archie MacIntyre, aged forty-five, and his twenty-one-year-old fiancée, Tina Carney, were rooting for Ellaway, and when the local boxer won the contest on points, the couple went to celebrate the victory at a local pub in St Paul's Square.

At this pub Archie was approached by a man who discreetly took him to one side, and then dropped a bombshell. He said that he had seen Tina with another man, leaving a Lime Street cinema on the previous Sunday. Archie, trying to remain calm, asked Tina for an explanation. Initially she denied that she'd been with another man, but Archie subsequently rummaged through her handbag and discovered a passionately penned love letter, addressed to Tina, and pinned to it was a photograph of an unknown young man.

She broke down and finally confessed to seeing a twenty-nine-year-old man from Cicero Terrace named Larry Thompson. Tina had met him at the Kempston Street factory where she worked, and had been seeing him secretly for about four months. To make matters worse, Tina had recently told Archie that she was pregnant and, as a result, he had obtained a huge loan from a moneylender to finance a lavish wedding.

Now Archie's hopes and dreams lay in tatters, thanks to some punk named

Thompson. Archie was renowned for his violent temper, and he swore to his older brother Frank that he would kill Thompson for wrecking his relationship with Tina. Archie had many contacts in Liverpool's underworld, and he soon managed to obtain a gun. Meanwhile, he kept Tina imprisoned inside a locked room in his home and dictated a letter she was forced to write to her secret lover.

With tears in her eyes, the broken-hearted girl wrote the letter and it was posted immediately. Larry received it the next day and read Tina's words. She wanted him to meet her at Arrad Street at the rear of the Hope Hall theatre on Tuesday night at half-past nine. At Archie's insistence, Tina wrote that she thought Archie was having her followed, and Arrad Street was the only place safe enough to meet.

Larry Thompson fell for it all, hook, line and sinker, and arrived at Arrad Street in his car. Archie lurked at the darker end of the street, wearing a pulled-down trilby and a dreary fawn gabardine suit. He watched the headlights of Thompson's car die shortly after the vehicle pulled up near the back of the theatre. Archie nervously felt for the cold metal of the pistol in his coat pocket as he waited.

Eventually, out of the gloom of Arrad Street, came the youthful figure of Larry Thompson. He looked exactly as he looked in the photograph which he'd found in Tina's possession. His rival in love seemed to walk rather unsteadily down the unlit street, until he was about ten feet away. Archie then withdrew the pistol from his coat pocket and aimed it at the figure. Larry threw up his arms defensively with a look of horror on his face, as he stared at the gunman. Archie fired the pistol three times – right at Larry's chest area. The bullets went straight through him and chipped the brickwork of the wall on the left side of the street. Larry clutched his chest and seemed to be in shock. Archie swiftly turned and ran across Hope Street, down Maryland Street, before nipping down South Hunter Street, where his car was parked in an unlit corner.

They say that the criminal always returns to the scene of his crime, and that's exactly what Archie did. After hurling the pistol into the River Mersey at the Pier Head, Archie motored around the night streets for a while, then drove up Oxford Street and slowed down as he passed Arrad Street. He could see Larry Thompson's car, still in the exact same spot where the dead man had parked it. There was no sign of a policeman, or any sort of activity and that baffled Archie.

When he arrived home he broke out into a cold sweat. He was a mess. His brother Frank told him not to worry, as he and five associates would swear in court that they had been playing poker with him at the time of the shooting. He reminded Archie that Tina had been warned that she'd be knifed if she opened her mouth. Archie steadily went to pieces. His hands started to shake uncontrollably and he kept on repeating that he should not have taken a man's life just because he had been betrayed in love. Archie even talked about going to the police station to turn himself in, but Frank reminded him that he'd hang if he did that, and he plied his trembling brother with several glasses of neat scotch to calm his nerves.

In the bedroom upstairs, Tina wailed, knowing that a terrible revenge had been exacted upon her lover.

Frank and Archie sat up all that night expecting a heavy knock at the door, but none came. Every page of the Liverpool Echo and other newspapers was scanned by the two men on the following day, but they could find no mention of a murder in Liverpool. Frank asked his younger brother if he was sure he'd hit Larry and Archie said he had definitely blasted him in the chest. It was highly unlikely that any man could have survived being shot in the chest at such close range. Archie said that he even remembered seeing the bullets hit the wall behind Larry, so they could not have been blanks.

That evening, Archie and Frank discovered to their horror that Tina had somehow managed to escape from the room upstairs by climbing out of the window on to a shed in the back yard. The girl dashed to the nearest police station and within minutes, detectives and constables were paying Archie and Frank a visit. The two brothers had no alternative but to open the door to them. The men were quizzed at the police station, and a detective asked Archie why he had kept Tina confined against her will in the bedroom. Archie assumed that Tina had also told the police how she had been forced to write Larry Thompson a letter, luring him to the ambush in Arrad Street. He also presumed that the man's body had been found, so he blurted out his confession to the shooting. "It was a crime of passion," he said, with a tremor in his voice. "I shot Larry Thompson."

The police looked at one another, baffled. Larry Thompson had not been shot. He was certainly dead, there was no question about that, but there was not a scratch upon his body. Naturally, Archie was confused on hearing this. The police said that Larry Thompson had died from a rare heart condition called cardiomyopathy, which often affects young people. He had died in his car just after he had parked it in Arrad Street.

After issuing Archie with a warning never to go near Tina again, the detective angrily added that wasting police time was a serious offence, and he told him to beat it. The detective assumed that Archie had somehow learned of Larry's death, and had then subjected Tina to psychological torture by pretending that he had killed her lover. The letter Tina had written to Larry, asking him to come to Arrad Street was not dated, so the police disregarded it.

Archie later visited Arrad Street with his brother and showed him the three bullet marks in the wall, but there were no signs of any bullets. The brothers left the street, and just before they drove away, Frank broke the silence. He turned to his brother and said, "I wonder if you shot a ghost?" Archie was rather taken aback by the question. Frank hypothesised that perhaps when Larry had died of natural causes in the car, his ghost had left the vehicle in an effort to keep its appointment with Tina, and perhaps it was this apparition that Archie had shot. The bullets had indeed travelled through the ghost's chest and hit the wall behind it, but the ghost – being already dead – could not be killed. Archie had immediately turned and fled, assuming he'd killed a flesh and blood person. Archie remembered that Larry had reflexively thrown up his arms as he opened fire on him. Frank speculated that perhaps at that point Larry had not even realised that he was dead, and had therefore thrown his arms up in fright at the sight of the gun.

The MacIntyre brothers said a prayer for Larry at a church on the way home, and the strange incident caused them to undergo a change of heart which gradually led them to turn their backs on crime.

THE GHOST THAT CASED JOINTS

The following tale is bizarre but is catalogued in the annals of the Psychical Research Society in London. The incident allegedly happened in Liverpool in the 1950s.

In 1951, a burglar broke into an office in Speke, opened the safe, and stole about £900. The police were baffled. It looked like an inside job because the thief had evidently known the combination of the safe. The police forensic officer managed to extract part of one thumbprint on the safe door. The next evening, again in Speke, a post office was broken into and the safe opened by someone who again knew the combination. This time, £1000 was taken. This time the police uncovered a thumb and fingerprint on the door and matched the print to that on the office safe. The following week, a thief broke into the premises of a betting shop in Halewood and emptied the safe, which was hidden in the concrete floor under a desk. The fingerprints on the desk matched the prints at the other crime scene but the police were baffled by the burglar's modus operandi; how could he have known the combinations of all three safes?

The case took a bizarre twist when a young woman who had been a counter clerk at the burgled post office, was being cross-questioned by two detectives. She was asked to go through all the trivial events of her working day, when she suddenly said, "Oh, yes! The ghost".

The slightly bemused detectives asked her to explain what she meant and she gave her account of what she had seen.

"I came in earlier than usual and when I went to the back room where the safe was, I saw this ghastly face, white, with a thick black moustache. It seemed to come through the wall, high up in the corner, near the ceiling and it was looking at me with a surprised look. Within a blink it was gone and I thought I must have been seeing things."

The counter clerk had told no one about the weird experience because she feared being dismissed by her boss. The detectives promised the woman they would say nothing about her eerie encounter.

A week later, a clerk who had stayed behind at Martins Bank in Liverpool to sort out the accounts of a local company, was startled to see the face of a man in the darkness behind him. The clerk swung his desk lamp up and shone it at the intruder, only to find that the face had disappeared. The bank clerk remembered, however, that the face had a thick black moustache. That evening, someone broke into the bank with a crowbar, bypassed the alarm by inserting a disabling key that had been hidden under a ledger and opened the safe. This time, a policeman on his beat entered the bank and collared the robber. The thief turned out to be George Johnson, a small-time pickpocket, originally from Preston. When Johnson was interrogated, he confessed to being responsible for the spate of safe robberies but when he told the police how he had known the combinations of the safes and other details, the detectives thought he must either be insane, or else pretending to be mad.

Johnson said the ghost of his recently-deceased partner-in-crime, Arthur Hennessy, had acted as his accomplice. Johnson explained that he was of Romany stock and was psychic, this ability enabling him to communicate with the ghost of his close mate who had died recently in a car crash. The ghost cased the joints and came back to tell him the combinations and where the safes were hidden. Police refused to believe Johnson's far-fetched tale but when they showed a photograph of his dead friend to the bank clerk and the post office counter clerk, the two witnesses agreed that it was identical to the ghostly face they had seen. The case took another twist, a week later, when George Johnson suffered a very heavy nosebleed, dying minutes later, apparently from natural causes.

No one was tried for the baffling safe robberies and the crimes ceased upon Johnson's death. Police gave little publicity to the case – for which they had no rational explanation to offer.

THE ULTIMATE ANSWER

This is a bizarre story about guilt, curiosity and deadly knowledge. There is a certain series of streets near Goodison Park which infer specific words. The streets: Oxton, Wilmslow, Eton, Neston, Andrew, Nimrod, Dane, Wilburn, Ismay, Lind, Lowell, Index, Arnot, Makin, and so on in line, spell out, very distinctly, the words 'Owen and Williams'. In actual fact, Owen and Williams was the name of the firm of builders who built those very streets. A major shareholder in this firm was a Lancashire millionaire named Henry Williams.

Williams had become a millionaire after his father had died and left him his fortune. He felt immense guilt over his sudden wealth, which rumour has it may have been brought on after he heard a sermon by a Welsh Presbyterian minister in 1886. Around this time, Mr Williams' behaviour became very erratic. He became completely fixated with the concept of death and started spending most of his time in and around hospitals. Specifically, he started to visit the Southern Hospital in Liverpool on a regular basis. In one instance he went over to a dying girl and sat with her, holding the sick little girl's hand as she passed away. Mr Williams softly stroked her frail hand, as if in a daze, he repeatedly urged, "What can you see?" The staff became concerned by the distracted man's persistent questions and eventually an alert nurse beckoned the doctor on the ward to literally throw Mr Williams out of the hospital grounds.

As the weeks went on, Williams's obsession with dying and what lies beyond the present life intensified. He talked at length with priests, vicars and ministers of every denomination and found that none of them could answer his question: what was it like after death?

It was not until he visited an equally eccentric man, a Dr McCheyne, and discussed the nature of death and the next world with him, that Mr Williams saw a potential solution to his inquiry. Dr McCheyne suggested something that today would have had him struck off the medical register. The eccentric doctor stated that he was confident that he had the means to stop Henry Williams' heart for a set period of time. He went on to claim that he could then revive him. He explained that he believed that this borderline between life and death, when the heart ceased beating and the brain became starved of oxygen, was the moment when many patients who were later resuscitated had reported intriguing glimpses of the 'next world'.

Amazingly, Williams became excited beyond belief at the prospect of his curiosity being satisfied once and for all, and hurriedly agreed to the highly unethical and dangerous experiment. Attended by a nurse, Dr McCheyne used ether and a solution of cocaine to bring Williams' heart to a halt. That part of the experiment ran smoothly, it was the restarting of his heart that became problematic. As Williams turned bluer by the minute, Dr McCheyne massaged his heart in utter desperation. There was still no response and Dr McCheyne became distraught as the clock ticked away. If left much longer, the brain would suffer irreversible damage and death would inevitably occur.

The nurse became increasingly anxious. She was all too aware of just how illegal an operation they were involved in, and shuddered at the fact that Dr McCheyne could well be imprisoned for such an unethical experiment and that she too could be tried for aiding and abetting him. After six seemingly endless minutes of electrified suspense and foreboding, the nurse detected a faint pulse in Henry Williams' wrist. His heart started to beat again, feebly at first, but gradually getting stronger. As he regained consciousness, the millionaire's body went into spasm, and he then proceeded to vomit, violently and uncontrollably.

Some thirty minutes later, Williams was calmer and was able to relate a very strange tale indeed. He described how he had travelled along a tunnel towards a bright and startling light, which is an overused description we hear regularly nowadays from people who have had a near-death encounter. Williams went on to explain how he had then found himself walking up large stone steps that were flanked on each side by huge pillars. At the top of this staircase there had stood a being, an amorphous snow-white column of immense power which gave off a terrific roar that sounded like a gigantic waterfall. He stated that it was God, claiming that he could not explain how he knew this, just that he had sensed it with an indisputable certainty.

Williams proceeded to give details about the figures he had seen coming down the stairs; they were faceless people draped in long, flowing gowns. These presences were in a limbo of some sort, but again Williams could not explain how he knew this. He claimed that at the top of the steep staircase, he communicated with God, which he described as feeling as if he was a vortex of

41

life-giving energy. Williams went on to describe how he had told the force that he had come to Him for knowledge.

It was at this stage of his account that Williams became anxious. He stuttered as he explained how God had duly given him an overwhelming reply, which he described as the answer to everything – the meaning of life – contained in a single sentence of just seven words. The nurse and doctor waited and watched, enthralled by what they were hearing.

Apparently, the next thing that Williams had known was that he was alive again and recovering in the doctor's private room. As he sat up, he stared back at his dumbstruck companions with his eyes wide. He became visibly agitated as he struggled to remember what the all-important knowledge he had received from the other side had been. Just moments later, with a look of sheer horror on his face, he slowly recalled what the momentous message had been, and animatedly recited the compact sentence to the nurse and doctor.

Events then took a very sinister turn. Within just one week, the nurse had allegedly committed suicide and the doctor was certified as insane. Williams is said to have told his secret to only six other people, each of whom supposedly also died within the year. Only one man who heard those seven mind-boggling words is said to have survived, a psychical research scientist, Sir Oliver Lodge.

Williams was also committed to a lunatic asylum and died from an epileptic fit eighteen months later. When the strangely linked deaths became public knowledge, religious mania was blamed. A persistent rumour circulated at the time, that the seven words of the so-called, 'ultimate answer' were written on seven separate pages and placed in a secret place. Be careful you don't ever stumble across them!

Mr Sphinx

One stormy evening at Woolton Hall in 2003, I gave an illustrated talk on the subject of the supernatural, which included several tales on the subject of vampires. After the talk, Susan, a distinguished-looking woman of eighty, approached me and told me how much she had enjoyed the stories and slide show pictures. She then related an intriguing story of her own that was as good, if not better, than any of the tales I'd been telling to people that evening. This is the account she gave.

Susan was born in Northumberland in 1923, and her mother, a teacher of English and Latin, brought Susan to Liverpool in 1933. Susan's father had deserted her mother just before the girl's birth. In the leafy lanes of suburban Aigburth, ten-year-old Susan and her mother settled into a beautiful house on Waverley Road. However, the rent for the fine residence was barely covered by the money Susan's mother brought in from her job as a private tutor.

In the autumn of 1933, a tall, smartly-dressed stranger with coal-black hair and penetrating green eyes called at the house, and told Susan's mother, in a foreign accent, that he would like to learn how to speak English. The man's name, Raymond Sphinx, struck Susan as being rather odd to say the least. Susan's mother explained that many foreigners choose their own names to replace their real, exotic-sounding surnames, in order to blend in to the country they are living in. Mr Sphinx was quite handsome, and as Susan related this tale, she recalled how her mother seemed totally mesmerised by the debonair foreigner, who seemed to be about thirty-five years of age. He was so courteous and sophisticated, and must have been an excellent student, as he was soon speaking with a fine, mellifluous English accent.

Children are very perceptive and discerning when it comes to seeing through the pretensions of adults, and young Susan thought there was something decidedly uncanny about Mr Sphinx. He seemed to appear out of nowhere whenever he visited for his lessons, and throughout the early summer of 1934, Susan watched him walk out on to a veranda – and when she followed, he had vanished. When she mentioned this to her mother, she was accused of having an overactive imagination.

Some time later though, Susan's mother said she too had seen Raymond walk on to the veranda and then seemingly disappear into thin air. She even mentioned the incident to him on the following day, but he just smiled his enigmatic smile and said that he had slipped past her but she hadn't noticed him. Susan's mother said nothing, but knew that simply had not been the case at all.

Mr Sphinx continued to come to the house, long after he needed to, as he now spoke English as perfectly as Susan's mother. Then it slowly dawned on Susan that her mother was romantically involved with the foreigner, and on many nights she would listen to him as he sat at the piano in the drawing room, bringing forth soul-stirring concertos of Mozart and Beethoven. Some of the other, unknown melodies sounded mysterious and romantic, and they brought tears to the eyes of Susan's mother.

The multi-talented Mr Sphinx was also an amazing storyteller, and on winter evenings he would sit before a blazing coal fire with Susan by his side and tell her tales of kings, queens, and ordinary people of long ago. He would also describe the daring missions of King Arthur and his Knights of the Round Table, and a saga about two young lovers on opposing sides during the Wars of the Roses. Raymond told these stories with such skill, that his listeners almost believed they were actually there, in the midst of the romance and intrigue.

Susan's mother's liking for Mr Sphinx must have waned, because she became involved with another man in 1936, and Raymond decided to leave but, before he went, he produced a single blood-red rose, backed with maidenhair fern and gave it to thirteen-year-old Susan, who was heart-broken at the idea of him leaving her life. Raymond whispered the word 'Zuzana' – an old Slavic word for the rose – and said that he would return one day when she was older, and declared that his love for her was undying. He said that the rose he had given her would never die, just like the affection he felt for her. With a tear in his eye, he said, "Remember me," then left, and Susan began to sob. She begged her mother to leave her lover and to resume her relationship with Raymond, but to no avail.

The rose which Mr Sphinx had given to Susan refused to wilt, and she kept it in a special box. World War Two came and went, and still the red rose and maidenhair fern looked as fresh as the day he had given them to her.

In 1948, at the age of twenty-five, Susan married a thirty-one-year-old man named Ralph, and moved with him just around the corner from her mother, to live over the grocery shop he owned. Susan's mother was ill at this time, and her condition was exacerbated by the anger she felt towards Susan for "marrying beneath herself" as she put it, and the heartbreak she was enduring because her lover had deserted her for a much younger woman.

Weeks later, Susan's mother died from pulmonary complications, and only Susan, Ralph and a doctor were at her bedside. About a fortnight after the funeral, Susan went to the cemetery alone to place flowers on her mother's grave, and during the visit she had an encounter that initially shocked her. A tall man dressed in black was already standing at the foot of her mother's grave. He turned as Susan approached. It was Raymond Sphinx, and he looked as if he hadn't aged a day since she last saw him in 1936, twelve years ago. He stood there with a faint smile on his lips; his arms outstretched to embrace Susan. He hugged and kissed her, and offered his deepest condolences. He assured her that her mother had merely shed her physical body, and that her soul had gone on to another plane of existence, where every person ends up when earthly life ceases.

Susan felt an intense physical and romantic attraction to Raymond, and she asked him to accompany her to her late mother's home on Waverley Road. At the house where Raymond had first met Susan as a child, she showed him the box containing the undying rose. Raymond embraced Susan and kissed her passionately. Not long afterwards they were making love, and throughout the act, Susan felt all her energy steadily draining away.

When the couple had finished making love, Susan felt numb and empty, and so listless, she could hardly make the effort to draw breath. A strange thought crossed her lethargic mind: had Raymond somehow siphoned off the very essence of her life force? Her lover leaned on his elbow beside her, and scanned her face, then put his palm on her forehead. Susan felt a distinct sensation of something in flux passing between his hand and her mind. Energy flowed down her spine and a strange cold tingling sensation coursed down her arms and legs.

After a while, Raymond removed his palm and then kissed Susan's cheek. She raised herself up and asked him what had just happened. She was more fascinated than afraid. She had never experienced such intense electric pleasures when her husband had made love to her. What Raymond told her shocked her to her core. Sphinx explained that he was a "type of vampire". He was nothing like the Dracula character of the Bram Stoker novel. He didn't suck blood, but he did "feed" off the life force of people – 'prana'.

Susan found herself putting on her dress without bothering to put on her underwear first. She trembled as Raymond sat at end of the bed with his head bowed and knew that he wasn't mentally unbalanced. She also knew he wasn't just trying to frighten her – he was telling the truth – she could tell by that look of sincerity in his green eyes.

"Please don't go, Susan," he said meekly.

The everlasting rose flashed into her mind. Of course! – now it all made sense. All those tales of long ago that Raymond had told around the fireside when she was a child. No wonder he had been able to make them sound so realistic – he must have been walking the earth for hundreds of years! Was he some kind of devil?

Susan didn't stop to look back as she hurried out of the bedroom in a panic, clutching her shoes. She walked barefooted down the road and only put the shoes on once she had turned the corner, from where she walked in shock back to her home above the greengrocer's. Ralph didn't even notice that her hair was in disarray, her lipstick smudged and her clothes dishevelled. Susan didn't return to her former home on Waverley Road until the next day, and when she did, she made sure that a friend went with her. She need not have worried – Raymond had gone.

In 1977, at the age of fifty-four, Susan was out shopping in Liverpool city centre when, just as she was leaving Binn's department store, she came face to face with Raymond. He still looked around thirty-five, with not a single wrinkle on his handsome face, or grey hair on his head. His green eyes sparkled as keenly as ever. He didn't recognise her at first, and he walked on past – but then he hesitated, and turned around. Not a word was spoken for a frozen moment in time. Then, as if he hadn't seen Susan for just a few days, he asked her how she was, and reached out for her hand – but Susan pulled away. He then suggested going to a nearby café, but Susan resolutely shook her head. Raymond seemed to sense that she was worried over something, and asked if her husband was well. Susan didn't answer. Instead, she turned and walked away, as Raymond shouted her name three times. She resolutely ignored him and walked away towards the safety of the crowds milling in and out of Woolworths.

In the Northern Hospital that evening, Susan's husband Ralph was lying in a bed, drifting in and out of a comatose state with a blood clot on his brain. The doctors had told Susan that he was in a critical condition and there was a high probability that he would not pull through. It had already been explained to her that brain surgery would be far too risky in Ralph's weakened condition.

At home, Susan fastened the top and bottom bolts of the front door, and locked her back door. Not only was she totally distraught about her husband's grave condition, but also deeply troubled about the meeting with Raymond, after all those years. She also wondered if the eerie Raymond had somehow followed her home. She took an old Bible up to the bedroom and sat up in bed, listening to the radio. She reached for the old Bible and opened it at random. She scanned a passage about the transfiguration of Christ, and for some reason it made her think about Raymond. With shame, she recalled the strange, unearthly sensations she had experienced when she was in the bed with him all those years ago, and of that mysterious word he spoke – 'prana'.

At almost three in the morning, Susan drifted into a fitful sleep that was haunted by dreams of Raymond. At eight o'clock the bell of the alarm clock sounded, and she swung her legs out of the bed like an automaton, with her eyelids still stuck together. With a sinking feeling in the pit of her stomach, she went downstairs to the hall, still in her nightdress, and telephoned the hospital. She feared the worst and dreaded to hear what they would say about her husband's condition.

She was in for a massive shock. The sister on duty said that she had some very good news. Ralph was no longer on the critical list; in fact, he was sitting up in bed, eating a hearty breakfast and laughing and joking with all the nurses. He had made a recovery that was nothing short of miraculous.

Susan was dressed and ready within half an hour of hearing this wonderful news and was soon riding in a cab to the hospital. Bursting with excitement, she rushed into the room where Ralph had lain at the gates of death for almost a month … and found the bed empty. The other bed in that room, in which a young man had been recovering from a spinal injury, was also vacant. Then she heard the sound of footsteps in the corridor to her right. It was Ralph, walking along with a nurse on either side of him, supporting him as he walked along. When he saw Susan he stopped in his tracks, and she ran to him with tears welling in her eyes. She hugged him so tightly, and he kept saying, "There, there, love," as he patted her on the back.

The nurses seemed to be just as overjoyed as they were – such miraculous recoveries happened so rarely. They showed Susan and Ralph into the two-bed ward, then left to give them some privacy. Ralph told Susan a tale that made her stomach somersault. He said that a "funny-looking man" had come into his room some time after midnight. He had walked over to Pete – the young man who was lying asleep in the other bed – and had placed his hands on the young man's chest. Ralph had been barely conscious, and the whole thing had a dream-like quality. The man – who was dressed in black – then came over to Ralph's bed and placed his palms on his chest. The intense heat from the stranger's hands penetrated right through his pyjamas, and his vest, straight into his heart. Ralph felt his entire body tingling, as if he had been plugged into the electricity mains. The man then assured Ralph that he would get better soon, then left the room in absolute silence – just like a ghost.

At six o'clock in the morning, Ralph opened his eyes, feeling like a new man. He sat up, stretched and yawned, and found a Catholic priest, a doctor and three relatives surrounding the bed of the man opposite, who was obviously dying. The priest was performing the Last Rites and Pete died soon afterwards.

"You don't believe me, do you?" Ralph said to Susan, who was staring at the single red rose, backed with a stem of maidenhead fern, lying on the bedside cabinet.

She knew exactly what had happened. Raymond – or whatever his real name was – had siphoned off the life of the young man in the other bed, and had infused that life into Ralph. Why had he done this? Susan still doesn't have any answers to this question.

Before Susan left Woolton Hall that stormy night, she told me that she was convinced that Mr Sphinx was still around.

"He will probably visit you if you put him in one of your books," she told me.

She then bade me goodnight, and a hackney cab took her off into the night.

GHOST OF CLAYTON SQUARE

HAUNTED LIVERPOOL 6

The following strange story was related to me by a very down-to-earth couple in Allerton. I have interviewed them and taped their story. In February 2000, Adam, a thirty-year-old man from Speke, left the Virgin Megastore in town with his friend Tony. The day was Monday, 14 February, Valentine's Day, and Adam's girlfriend Allison had asked him to buy a romantic video and a little gift for her. Nothing extravagant, just a little thing that would mean a lot.

Adam searched the shelves in the store but could not find a suitable video. Tony, getting increasingly bored, suggested *Last Tango in Paris*, but Adam said there was nothing romantic about the film. So, the two young men wandered off into Clayton Square Shopping Centre and found themselves outside the Body Shop.

"Do us a favour, Tony," Adam said. "I get completely flustered when I go into shops like this. Go and get me a basket of smellies, will you? I'll buy you a pint."

"No way! You must be joking! I'm not doing your dirty work for you."

"Ah! Go on, Tony. I won't have anything to give to Allison and I promised."

"You need to get a grip, mate. That Allison's got you round her little finger. She's turning you into a middle-aged bore. You never go to the match any more and what's happening to our Saturday night benders?"

"But me and Allison are saving ..." Adam began.

"Leave it out, Adam. You can stuff your smellies and your romantic videos. I'm off," snarled Tony.

He marched off angrily, leaving Adam lingering around the Body Shop window. Suddenly, a voice behind him said: "Hello there". The stranger was about twenty at the most, and had a mullet hairstyle with a feathered fringe and a parting down the middle of his head. He wore a distinctive black V-necked pullover, and on which there was a logo of a pouncing cat, and underneath, the word 'Slazenger'. His jeans were baggy at the top, but tapered inwards as they went down to his 'Gola' trainers.

Adam nodded back, then walked into the Body Shop to get away from the strange, out-dated looking youth. But the youth followed him and said something which stopped Adam in his tracks: "I used to go out with Allison Jones."

"What?" asked Adam, swinging round to face him.

"I saw you with her in the precinct with her the other day. She hasn't changed much."

"I'll mention you to her. What's your name?" Adam responded, unenthusiastically.

"Paul. Say Paul from High Park Street. Tell her I was asking," the youth replied.

"When were you seeing her?" Adam asked, not really enjoying this conversation with one of Allison's ex-boyfriends.

Paul said that he had gone out with Allison from when she was thirteen, until she was fifteen. As she was now twenty-six, this meant that he had dated her from 1987 to 1989, about twelve years ago. Adam felt dubious about this character asking about his Allison. He was surprised to find that he seemed to know everything about the girl's family, and her friends.

Suddenly Adam had what he thought was a bright idea. He asked Paul if he would go into the Body Shop and buy a gift for Allison. He admitted that he had a hang up about asking for feminine things in shops. Paul nodded amenably and went into the store and soon came out with the basketful of lotions and creams.

Adam thanked him.

"How come you're not buying your girl something today? It's Valentine's Day you know," he said.

Paul seemed choked up all of a sudden, and his eyes became watery. He simply shrugged and said nothing. Adam suspected that he had probably just come out of a relationship. He felt awkward, realising that he had been tactless. Trying to lighten the mood, he laughed and said to Paul, "She wanted me to get her a romantic video, but I couldn't find anything. I was thinking of getting her a 'Forever Friends' teddy bear, a big one. You could go in and get it for me if you want."

"She used to have a cabbage patch doll called Trudy," said Paul.

"Wait till I tell her all this, she'll go bright red," giggled Adam. "Trudy!"

"There were two films she loved. One was *ET*," Paul suggested.

"That's years old," Adam frowned.

"When ET used to say 'beee goood', then point to his heart and say, 'I'll be right here,' she always used to cry."

Unconvinced, Adam said, "Nah, she's seen that film about fifty times. What was the other video she liked?"

"An old black and white film. It was called *A Guy Named Joe*. It was about a pilot from the Second World War who died, but he comes back from heaven to help the boyfriend of the girl he left behind."

"I'm not getting her a black and white film, she'd go mad."

All of a sudden, Adam noticed that Paul was silently crying. Tears rolling down his cheeks. Before he could ask him what was wrong, the youth turned and walked away. He vanished round a corner and never returned. Adam searched for him, but could not find him anywhere.

When Adam went home to Allison, he told her about Paul from High Park Street, and she seemed to go numb with shock. She said he could not possibly have spoken to Paul, because he had been killed in a car crash in Widnes years ago – on Valentine's Day. Adam's stomach turned over when she told him this; she even produced an old photograph of Paul, and it was the same person he had spoken to in Clayton Square. Allison admitted that she did once have a cabbage patch doll named Trudy, and yes, she always cried at the end of *ET*. She also recalled that in her teenage days, her favourite romantic film had been *A Guy Named Joe*, so Adam managed to get a copy of the film and cradled an emotional Allison in his arms as they watched it.

THE GREY LADY OF ALLERTON TOWER

One autumnal afternoon several years ago, whilst writing and researching a volume of *Haunted Liverpool*, I decided to take a much-needed break, having been hunched over my computer for most of the day. I set off for a walk which took me down Menlove Avenue, past Calderstone's Park and into another, almost deserted park, where I dwelt upon the gothic splendour of Allerton Tower's ruins. I strolled through the vestiges of the palatial home which I knew had once belonged to the illustrious Earle family; the magnificent remnants of a legendary grandiose residence, now sadly left to the mercy of the English weather, idiotic vandals and mindless graffiti 'artists'.

As I lingered near the shell of an outbuilding on the long-lost, seventy-eight-acre estate of Allerton Tower, something just glimpsed out the corner of my eye flitted past me. I half-turned reflexively, but the flitting 'thing' had vanished, leaving a sweet scent in its wake. I immediately wondered if the fabled Grey Lady of the ruins had just brushed past me. I certainly had not imagined that entity and it had not been a trick of the light. Some ghosts are quite timid, and manifest themselves so briefly that they come and go in the twinkling of an eye. The Grey Lady of the ruins has been seen by numerous witnesses over the years, and several years ago I was told the tragic story which lay behind the haunting of Allerton Tower.

In the 1850s, Sir Hardman Earle lived at Allerton Tower, along with his five daughters, Elizabeth, Mary, Harriet, Emily and Georgina, and his three troublesome sons, thirty-five-year-old Thomas, twenty-two-year-old Arthur and seventeen-year-old William. Sir Hardman Earle, a super-rich, highly-influential director of the Liverpool to Manchester Railway, and the person after whom Earlestown, in Newton-le-Willows, was named, harboured many dark secrets and skeletons in his cupboards, and some in the upper echelons of Lancashire society believed there were many controversial questions marks hanging over the source of Hardman's vast wealth.

One summer evening, the three Earle sons left the grounds of Allerton Tower on the pretext of taking an evening stroll, and without their father's knowledge, for he would have been furious had he known, they visited a local tavern in

Woolton, where three local girls quickly fell for the wealthy trio. Thomas Earle had a wife at home, but periodically felt a craving which compelled him to go in search of the local maidens.

Upon this humid summer night, the three brothers went too far with their lustful desires, and in the deserted fields of Allerton, each of them ended up making love to the girls they had befriended at the tavern. Thomas and Arthur Earle were soon bidding their conquests a hasty goodnight after they'd taken their pleasure, but young intoxicated William, upon losing his virginity, was rashly declaring his intention to bring his lowly-born lover Mary home with him to meet their father. Upon hearing this preposterous suggestion, the two older brothers panicked and wrestled William away from the girl, then dragged him back home to Allerton Tower, where they tried everything in their power to quash all talk of infatuation.

However, William was not to be put off so easily and protested that he had fallen madly in love with his first conquest and that he was not prepared to abandon her, despite their protestations. From that day onwards, he seized every opportunity to sneak off from his father's sprawling mansion after dark to meet his beloved Mary; an Irish girl with beautiful blue eyes and long black hair. They became inseparable and planned to elope together, but somehow Sir Hardman Earle came to hear about the secret meetings and he gave his son a severe beating with his belt and had him confined to his rooms. The servants were given strict instructions to ensure that William stayed under lock and key. Sir Hardman also roundly criticised his older sons for leading young William astray.

Sometime afterwards, Mary was visited by Thomas Earle, who warned her to stay away from his teenaged brother, threatening her that if she knew what was good for her she would make sure she would never see him again. On hearing this, Mary began to cry bitterly, shyly confiding that she was already expecting William's child. Thomas was devastated by this new twist in the sad saga, realising that if word got out about the pregnancy it would create a scandal and bring shame on the whole family. Life at the Tower would not be worth living if that happened.

To make matters worse, the sobbing girl admitted that she had already told her Uncle Desmond about her condition, and he had immediately responded by saying that he would be going to visit Sir Hardman to demand some 'hush-money' to keep the disgraceful incident a secret. This latest admission made Thomas's blood run cold. How on earth had he let his brother fall into this trap from which there seemed to be no escape?

Thomas Earle returned to Allerton Tower and told no one about the news except his brother Arthur. They both understood that once blackmailers had got their teeth into their victims they would simply continue asking for more and more money, so the brothers decided on a drastic course of action. They would be forced to kill Mary and her uncle – there was no alternative.

One stormy night, young Mary was lured, unsuspecting, from her humble dilapidated home in Woolton Village by Thomas, the eldest of the Earle brothers, on the pretext that they needed to discuss the forthcoming birth of hers and William's child. She had received a note directing her to a secluded wood off a dirt track where Menlove Avenue now runs, and there she was ambushed and brutally bludgeoned to death by Thomas and Arthur Earle, who had been lying in wait for her. Arthur sobbed uncontrollably when he saw what he and his brother had done to the petite pregnant girl, but Thomas, who had inherited a greater measure of his father's ruthlessness, slapped him across the face and told him to stop his crying; their brother's welfare and the reputation of the Earle family was at stake. This was no time for regrets and faint heartedness, he argued, the girl was nothing but a slut, who deserved no better, and they had had no alternative but to kill her.

Arthur managed to compose himself sufficiently to help his brother carry the girl's limp and mangled body across a field at the far end of which they dropped it into the depths of an old well.

On the following evening, Desmond, the uncle of the murdered girl, was run down by a horse ridden by a man dressed in a long black cloak with a pulled-down hat-brim covering most of his face. Desmond died from his injuries several hours later without regaining consciousness. Then the body of Mary was hauled from the well, and most people assumed that she had accidentally fallen to her death, because the well had no protective wall around it, whilst others quickly suspected foul play, arguing that the two deaths, on consecutive nights, simply could not be put down to coincidence.

Some gypsy families were living in the area at the time, and Sir Hardman Earle suspected that they might have something to do with Mary's death, but one of the Romany men, whose surname was Wryme, eager to rid his community of suspicion, declared that he would be able to locate and identify the murderer of the Irish girl by the use of a divining rod. Soon afterwards, Wryme, followed by an assorted crowd of curious locals, assembled at the well where Mary's body had been discovered. He walked from the well with the dowsing rod in his hands pointing the way. The rod noticeably twitched up and down several times, and, to the delight of the onlookers, Wryme would occasionally spit out blood as he picked up the psychic scent of the killer. The gypsy walked in a straight line across the waterlogged fields of Woolton, with the crowds of sensation seekers growing behind him as he moved northwards from the well. Then Wryme's hands began to tremble violently as the rod reacted to something, and a wave of gasps coursed through the crowd as the Romany dowser approached Allerton Tower.

Two gardeners on the Earle estate tried to stop Wryme and the crowd, telling them that they were trespassing on private land, but the mob ignored him and crushed forward, determined to pursue the chase to the end; they hadn't enjoyed so much free entertainment since the last Sunday School outing. Before long Wryme reached the entrance to the Orangery of the colossal mansion, where he came face to face with the imperious figure of Sir Hardman Earle. When Wryme explained what he was doing, Sir Hardman became outraged. He turned on his heels, his whiskers bristling with indignation, and went to fetch several servants, also bringing with him two loaded pistols. The mob slowly began to disperse at the sight of the pistols and reluctantly started to walk back the way they had come. When Sir Hardman fired a pistol shot in the air as a warning, the retreat turned into a stampede; the locals being only too well aware of His Lordship's ruthless reputation.

But that was not the end of the matter. Some weeks later, the male members of the Hardman family began to reap the consequences of their terrible actions when the apparition of a beautiful, pale-faced girl with bedraggled wet hair and soaking wet clothes appeared first in the bedroom of Thomas Earle. She brought with her the weight of immeasurable sadness which seemed to fill the room and her ghost looked so solid, that Thomas felt he could reach out and touch it. He could even see water dripping off it on to the carpet. He wrung his hands and screamed out in terror, upon which the girl, whom he recognised at once as his brother's sweetheart whom he had so savagely murdered, vanished into the night air.

Shortly afterwards, Arthur Earle was also visited by the dripping phantom. She appeared at his bedside at four o'clock in the morning. This time the girl's ghost was groaning in agony from the terrible wounds to her head and body and with a steady gaze, pointed an accusing finger at Arthur. By the time she had disappeared he had been reduced to a jibbering wreck and would never enjoy a peaceful night's sleep again.

The spectre persecuted the two brothers for many years, and was also said to have made an appearance of a more benign kind before her lover William Earle when he was a soldier, in 1885, on the eve of his death in the Sudan. She had also appeared to his father, Sir Hardman Earle, as he lay on his deathbed in 1877.

Since that time, the ghost of the murder victim has been seen on many occasions treading forlornly among the ruins of Allerton Tower, and she is now known as the Grey Lady of Allerton Tower.

THE BLOKE

The following incident took place at a certain house in Liverpool in 1985. The ghost featured in the story is still active but as the people who currently live in the haunted house are not yet aware that they have a ghost on their premises, the street cannot be mentioned in the story. This ghost could be in the house next door to you, or it could even be in your house. However, don't worry if Jarvis is with you now, because he's a very friendly and helpful ghost.

In the late summer of 1985, a twelve year-old boy named Alex was sitting having breakfast with his family when, suddenly, a jar of marmalade in front of him slid a few inches across the tablecloth, startling everyone. The boy's parents and seven year-old sister were naturally quite astonished, but Alex just smirked and whispered, "Stop it, Jarvis".

His mother's mouth dropped open and she looked at the marmalade jar, then looked at Alex.

"How did you do that?" she asked.

"I didn't, Mum," protested Alex. "Jarvis did it."

"Who?" asked Alex's father, who had been reading the newspaper.

"The bloke from upstairs," Alex replied, and carried on eating his cornflakes.

"Eh? What bloke, son?" Alex's father was very intrigued by his son's comments and wanted an explanation.

Alex had a lot of explaining to do.

"Well, Dad, this bloke comes into my room at night. He tells me stories sometimes and he looks as if he's a ghost, 'cos you can see through him. He's like a fuzzy shadow and I told him that I'd never tell anyone about him. He said he's French and his name's Jarvis something. I can't remember his second name. It isn't Smith or anything like that."

Alex's parents looked at each other, not knowing whether to laugh or be concerned. Alex's sister, Kelly, giggled and put her hand to her mouth.

"Stop telling porkies, Alex," she said. "There's no bloke upstairs in your room. Stop giving him pocket money, Dad, 'cos he's telling lies."

That night, Alex's Dad left his bedroom to go to the toilet and, as he walked past his son's bedroom, he heard a conversation. He thought his son was talking in his sleep, so he opened the door to look in and saw Alex sitting up in bed with his bedside lamp on. At the bottom of the bed there was an outline of a shady figure which vanished as soon as he looked at it. Alex's Dad turned the light on and looked in complete disbelief at the space at the end of Alex's bed where the ghostly figure had been just seconds before. He grabbed his son by the arm and yanked him out of bed, then dragged him to his bedroom, where he closed the door and put a chair against it. Alex's mum woke up and asked what all the noise was about.

"I saw it! I saw the ghost. He's bloody right! There is a ghost in his room! I can't believe what I saw."

"Oh calm down, Dad," said Alex. "It's okay. Jarvis is alright, honest."

"I'm frightened," said Alex's mother and she got up and turned the light on.

"Shall we stay over at your Mum's?" Alex's father asked his wife.

"Are you sure you weren't dreaming, love?"

"I know what I saw!" he shouted and suddenly there was a rapping at the door. Alex's parents both jumped and his mum let out a scream.

"Mummy," said a girl's voice. It was little Kelly. She had woken up with all the noise.

Kelly's parents opened the door and took her into their room.

"It's alright, Kelly. You can sleep with Mummy and Daddy tonight," said Kelly's mum.

"I'm tired, Dad," complained Alex. "I want to sleep in my own bed."

"No, you can't. There's a you-know-what in there," replied his father in a harsh voice.

He couldn't mention the word 'ghost' in case he scared Kelly, but he was the one who seemed to be the most terrified. The whole family spent the night in the same double bed and hardly got any sleep. Throughout the night, Alex's parents kept jumping at every little sound.

The following day, when the children were at school, they visited a Catholic priest. He was very sympathetic and said he himself had seen a ghost many years ago. He also told them that he thought he had some psychic powers. He promised he would visit the house in the evening and bless Alex's bedroom. The priest turned up and interviewed Alex in his bedroom for over an hour, taking notes throughout. After talking at length to the child, the priest came down to the living room and checked a few details that he had taken down in his notebook. He sat facing Alex's parents and Kelly and asked them, "Is it true that there was a break-in about three months back?"

"Yes," said Alex's father, "but nothing was taken. They broke in through the back door. Why?"

"And the robbers took nothing. Don't you find that unusual?" inquired the priest, scratching his head. He looked at Alex's parents over his spectacles.

"What do you mean?" remarked Alex's mum.

"According to your son, the ghost – Jarvis – scared the robbers away from the house," said the priest.

Alex's parents looked at each other in disbelief, and the priest quoted the other notes from his little black book.

"Erm, let me see. Then there was a chip pan that went on fire, but a damp tea-towel mysteriously put the fire out, even though no one remembers who put the towel on the fire? Then you, dear," the priest addressed little Kelly, "were playing in the street with Alex and ran out in front of a car to get an ice cream and something lifted you off your feet and pulled you out the path of the car. Is that true?"

"Oh yeah, Mum. That's right. I forgot," said Kelly.

"And you, sir?" the priest addressed Alex's father. "You recently lost your car keys, and looked everywhere for them and then found them on the roof of your car. Is that true?"

"Yes. That was weird but what are you driving at?" asked Alex's Dad.

"All the work of one ghost named Jarvis. Your son says he's a friendly ghost who looks after you all like a guardian angel. I can't exorcise good ghosts, only evil spirits. You'd be better just turning a blind eye to him. He's done you a lot of good."

The priest then chuckled and, after drinking a cup of tea, left the house.

Unfortunately, only Alex and Kelly could accept poor Jarvis and so Alex's cowardly parents moved their family from the house. According to Alex, on the last night in their house, he heard Jarvis crying.

In 1994, a window cleaner was cleaning the windows of the same house and almost fell off his ladder when he saw a semi-transparent figure coming towards him. The window cleaner was not aware that the house was haunted and now gets his colleague to clean the windows of that house instead.

In 1997, a new family moved into the house and are apparently oblivious of the friendly ghost's activities. It will be interesting to see how long this unsuspecting family can remain ignorant of their ectoplasmic 'helper'.

ARROWS IN THE SNOW

One blazing hot day in July 1815, the sailing ship Lothair glided into the Liverpool Docks having just crossed the Atlantic from North America. Amongst the gaggle of excited passengers who disembarked from the vessel that day was a rich Scottish merchant named John Allan, accompanied by his wife Frances, her younger sister Nancy, and the couple's rather sickly-looking six-year-old adopted son, Edgar.

The Allans were greeted on the dockside by Thomas MacKenzie – a cousin of William Mackenzie, the Scottish railway engineer entombed in the famous pyramidal tomb on Rodney Street. Thomas MacKenzie had secured the services of two trustworthy and hardworking Liverpool maidservants – Isabel Cook and Joan Slaidburn – to accompany the Allan family on their forward journey to Irvine in Scotland. Isabel's seven-year-old sister Mary joined the party and became a playmate for little Edgar, the Allans' adopted son, when they arrived in Scotland.

Just a week before Christmas, little Mary took it upon herself to go out into the nearby woods one snowy afternoon to collect holly and ivy with which to decorate the Allans' home. Young Edgar accompanied the Liverpool girl, and somehow managed to slip out of the cottage unnoticed – his parents tended to wrap the child in cotton wool and he would never have been allowed out in such inclement weather if they had known about Mary's plan.

The two children gambolled about in the snow like two puppies. It was such a relief to be out of doors in the fresh highland air. Edgar, in particular, was invariably cooped up inside the house and he envied the local children who had the freedom of the countryside. They had soon collected whole bunches of holly laden with berries and fruiting ivy and placed them in Mary's basket along with mountains of pine cones. Wouldn't everyone be pleased when they took them back home? There would be enough to decorate the whole house. They had just agreed that it was about time that they returned home, when a strange incident occurred.

An invisible hand – or foot – was mysteriously drawing a trail of arrows in the snow which lay thick and virginal on the ground. The two children looked on in astonishment as one arrow after another was traced in the snow. They followed the arrows, and at one point, Mary wrote "Who are you?" in the snow with the tip of her umbrella – and the invisible doodler sharply crossed out the question with three lines. This gave the children a start and made them feel uneasy, but their curiosity was even stronger than their fear and so they followed the arrows which continued to appear, one after the other, snaking through the wood until eventually they led to a small lake where the children had been forbidden to go.

Suddenly, Edgar realised that he and Mary had been lured on to the thin ice at the edge of the frozen lake. The ice creaked and groaned ominously, ready to give way, and Edgar just managed to seize Mary by the arm and drag her to safety in the nick of time. The children then heard the voice of an old woman cursing them from somewhere amongst the snow-laden branches of the trees which encircled the lake. They peered into the trees but could see no one, so they ran home as fast as their legs would carry them and told the adults what had happened. They both received a good telling off and were sent to bed without any supper, but it was obvious to the adults that something untoward had happened in the wood that afternoon, and Mary's seventeen-year-old sister Isabel set off to investigate the arrows, expecting to find some kind of animal tracks, probably those of a large bird.

However, almost as soon as she arrived in the wood she found the arrows – they really did exist after all – and she traced them, and the children's footsteps, through the trees and to the lake's edge. She was horrified to see that their footsteps actually went out on to the icy surface of the lake and she realised that they had had a very lucky escape. They could both so easily have fallen through the ice and drowned.

She was just about to retrace her steps back through the wood when she recoiled in horror – for there, barely visible under the thin icy surface of the lake, floated the lifeless face of a child – and the sight of it sent the servant screaming for help.

Police later discovered that the body of the unfortunate child trapped under the ice was that of six-year-old Carol McClean, a farmer's daughter who had been reported missing some days before. John Allan was of the opinion that the arrows had been drawn in the snow as a deliberate lure for the local children – a lure that would lead them to almost certain death. He was also convinced that they had been put there by the evil spirit of a witch known as Old Nelly.

Apparently, Old Nelly had been deliberately drowned in the lake by the local villagers over a hundred years ago, as a punishment for her witchcraft, which they felt was damaging their crops and bringing death and disease to themselves and their animals. A total of nine children had drowned in the lake since that time, most probably lured to their deaths by Old Nelly's evil sorcery. Mary Cook and Edgar Allan were therefore even more fervently warned to stay well away from that lake, and this time they needed no persuading.

Incidentally, Edgar Allan later grew up to become Edgar Allan Poe, the most famous horror-story writer of all time. Perhaps this early brush with the supernatural acted as a catalyst for his brilliant and fertile imagination.

THE GIRL IN THE RED DRESS

HAUNTED LIVERPOOL 10

In the severe winter of 1981, a newly ordained priest was at work in his study one night, struggling to write a sermon. Huge snowflakes drifted past the Elizabethan windows, adding a top layer to the heavy snowfall that had already blanketed the streets of Liverpool.

The priest, named Gary, had a number of newspaper clippings of interest on his desk, and had intended to use the topical material they contained for his oration. As he was trying to find ways to incorporate the snippets of information into the sermon, he was interrupted by the bell downstairs ringing three times. Who could be calling at half-past nine on such a bitter winter's evening? Gary wondered, as he fumbled his way downstairs in the dark. The housekeeper usually answered the door at such an hour but this was the one night she had taken off to visit a relative.

Father Gary opened the front door of the priest's house, and saw a little girl, only about eleven or twelve years of age, standing on the doorstep. She had long straight black hair, a pale white face, and a large pair of expressive blue eyes. She wore a beautiful long crimson dress, white socks and black buckled shoes.

In a loud and clear voice, the girl addressed the priest. She urged him to go at once to an address in West Derby, where a Mr Quinn needed to confess something urgently, because his time was near.

"I beg your pardon?" Father Gary said, startled at the girl's unusual request.

West Derby was outside of his parish, and he was concerned about what a girl of her age was doing out alone on such a snowy and bitterly cold night. The girl said nothing more, she simply turned and walked down the steps and turned right, back into the street. The priest walked down the steps after her. He wanted to check that she was safe, but he saw to his utter amazement that she had vanished. He looked down at the fresh layer of virgin snow on the front path, and immediately noticed that she had left no footprints. The priest was more astounded than scared. He walked back up the steps and into the hallway.

Father Gary made his way back up to his study, thinking about the strange experience he had just had. Unable to come up with of any rational explanation, he wondered what the official Church line was on ghosts. He scoured his bookshelves until his eye fell upon *The Catholic Encyclopaedia Dictionary* on the top shelf of the study bookcase. He flipped through the tome until he came to the entry for ghosts. It stated just this:

GHOST (noun). Catholic ideology has nothing to say against the possibility of a ghost, in the sense of an apparition of one who is dead. It is within the providence of God to permit departed souls to appear on earth to fulfil some good purpose, eg to give help or warning, or to obtain prayers.

The Church also fully recognises the possibility of apparitions or illusions caused by a diabolical agency.

His curiosity aroused, Father Gary decided to do a little research into whether there really was a Mr Quinn living at the address in West Derby given by the strange girl in the crimson dress. He reversed the car from its garage and drove carefully through the snow-carpeted roads and un-gritted black-iced lanes towards West Derby. At every red traffic light, the priest considered turning round and going home to finish his sermon instead of getting involved in what seemed to be a peculiar supernatural matter. Inquisitiveness overrode all such thoughts however, and just under thirty minutes later, he reached the house on Deysbrook Lane, West Derby. It was an expensive looking house, and children had built an impressive snowman in the garden.

The front door of the house opened as Father Gary left the car, and a petite middle-aged woman reached out to lower some empty milk bottles on to the step. She called out in a soft voice: "Modo, come on."

A cat padded softly out of a dark corner of the garden and scuttled into the lit hallway. The woman was about to close the door, when she then noticed the priest standing there. She said nothing, but merely stared as an expression of horror spread across her delicate looking face.

"Good evening. Would a Mr Quinn happen to live here?" Father Gary inquired, feeling awkward and somewhat foolish at the cause of his arrival.

The woman did not reply. She backed into the hallway without taking her eyes off the man before her. Her terror stricken face grew increasingly anxious as she moved backwards into the house and quickly slammed the door behind her.

Father Gary let out a sigh as he turned and went back to his car. He had told himself the notion was ridiculous. He revved his engine for a few seconds as he tried to move away, but his car had some difficulty starting, probably because of the arctic temperatures. When the car finally did start to move, Father Gary noticed a large, thickset man open up the front door again. The man hurried over to the priest's vehicle, and gestured for him to stop. Father Gary wound down his window.

"Did a girl send you here?"

The man's expression was also one of distress and fear.

Father Gary nodded, trying to work out what could possibly be making these two people look so terrified.

The man urged the priest to come into his home, and although reluctant, Father Gary agreed to his wish. Once inside the house, the man poured himself a large vodka with a trembling hand and proceeded to tell the priest a very strange story indeed.

Apparently, a year ago, he and three friends had been drinking heavily in a pub in Wales one evening. With alcohol tainting their judgement, the group foolishly decided to get into their van and set off to the next village to look for some local females. The van had woven unsteadily along a succession of winding and deserted lanes. On reaching a secluded lane, the drunken driver of the van was surprised when one of his friends shouted out for him to swerve. With alcohol-numbed reflexes, the driver was unable to follow the command and kept on moving forwards at considerable speed.

So befuddled was the driver that he remained unaware that he had just hit and killed a young girl. Her red dress had become entangled in the undercarriage of the van and her lifeless body was brutally dragged for a quarter of a mile under the vehicle. The men were genuinely ignorant of the appalling accident, assuming that the van had missed the figure in the road.

When the van was parked and the cold and sober light of day revealed that they had in fact hit the girl, the four men returned to Liverpool. Guilt-ridden, the men feared that their awful secret would surface with dire consequences, although nothing was ever reported. However, soon after, something very strange started to happen. One of the men, named Phil, received a knock on his door just after ten o'clock one night. He opened the door to be met by a priest, who announced that a small girl in a red dress had called at his church and begged him to visit Phil. The girl had claimed with adamance that Phil wanted to confess something before he died. Phil was not ready to confess to anything and insisted that priest leave his premises immediately. Curiously, Phil died in his sleep that very night. His lifeless face revealed a tortured expression that indicated he had suffered some kind of harrowing nightmare just before death.

The other two people who had been in that van on that murderous night both died some months later. They too had received sinister and unexpected visits from different priests, who also claimed to have been sent by a girl in a red dress.

"Are you Mr Quinn?" Father Gary asked with some caution.

The man nodded. He pleaded with the priest for an immediate confession in his kitchen, out of earshot of his wife. The penitent kneeled, and Father Gary listened. After the indepth confession, Mr Quinn shook hands with the priest and Father Gary asked him to come to his church on Sunday. He assured Mr Quinn and his wife that his confession had been heard and that nothing tragic was going to happen.

However, on the following day, Father Gary received a disturbing telephone call. Mrs Quinn's voice was choked as she explained to the priest that her husband had been declared dead on arrival at hospital early that morning. He had suffered a massive heart attack. Mr Quinn was just thirty-eight.

The unaccountable visit by the girl in red that snowy night has haunted Father Gary from that night onwards.

THE MARIE CELESTE CONNECTION

Most unsolved mystery buffs are familiar with the basic outline of the story of that fateful ship the *Marie Celeste*. She set sail from New York in November 1872 under the command of Captain Briggs with 1,700 barrels of crude alcohol in her hold, bound for Genoa in Italy. On board were Briggs' wife and two-year-old daughter and a crew of eight men.

Almost a month later, David Moorhouse, captain of a ship called the *Dei Gratia*, caught sight of a speck on the horizon, 500 miles east of the Azores. When he scrutinised it more closely through his telescope, he saw that it was a ship that was sailing erratically. He dispatched a boarding party over to investigate and they found the ship, the *Marie Celeste*, totally deserted. The only lifeboat was missing but, in all other respects, the ship was completely seaworthy.

There was a full six months' supply of food and water on the ship and also the crew's oilskins, boots, pipes and tobacco had all been left behind. It was obvious that everyone on board had left the ship in a tremendous hurry for some unknown reason. After an extensive search, it was discovered that only the navigation instruments appeared to have been taken. Further investigation revealed that someone had struck the ship's rail with an axe, or other sharp implement and, in the cargo hold, one of the barrels had been opened. The captain's sword was found on his bed in his cabin and, on a slate, someone had chalked the words, 'Fanny, my dear wife, Frances M R'.

Captain Moorhouse towed the derelict ship to Gibraltar and, after a lengthy court of enquiry, he was awarded a salvage cheque for the princely sum of £2000 for his troubles.

No one has ever fully solved the mystery of the *Marie Celeste* but quite a few people later came forward, claiming that they were survivors of the sea's most famous mystery. Most of these claimants were either publicity-seekers, or just plain conmen, out to make a quick buck. But, curiously, two Liverpool sailors were amongst those who claimed to have been on board the *Marie Celeste* during her fateful last voyage.

One of these was a ninety-two-year-old cook from Maryland Street named Lawrence Keating. He claimed that he had joined the crew at the last minute when one of the original sailors on the *Marie Celeste* refused to set sail because he believed in the ancient superstition that it was unlucky to embark on a merchant voyage with a woman on board (in this case the captain's wife). Keating's account detailed how the ship ran into a hurricane in the mid-Atlantic, which almost turned the ship on its end. During the storm, the piano on board came loose from its moorings and crushed the captain's wife leaving the captain utterly devastated by his terrible loss.

Adamantly refusing to confine his wife's decomposing body to the sea, he placed her in the only lifeboat and towed it by rope, behind the *Marie Celeste*. This action caused deep consternation amongst the crew and somebody eventually severed the rope and a fight resulted. The captain then went on the rampage, wielding an axe and threatening everyone in sight. After killing most of the crew, and with the storm still raging, he was washed into the sea. Keating had allegedly survived the whole incident by hiding in the cargo hold. However, no one believed his bizarre story and he died two months after his revelations, so his account could be neither authenticated, nor dismissed.

Another Scouser, William Foyle, a notorious thief and confidence-trickster, literally leapt aboard a ship named the *City of Ragusa* bound for Boston, in 1870. Billy Foyle was an inventive and imaginative conman, who was in the habit of selling fake maps of South African diamond mines to the gullible public. When he arrived in America, he embarked on a further series of frauds and, eventually, when the American authorities began to close in on his illegal, entrepreneurial activities, in order to evade capture, he allegedly stowed away on a brig – the *Marie Celeste*.

Now, Billy Foyle had gained such a well-deserved reputation from telling so many whoppers, that no one attempted to believe his version of the *Marie Celeste* mystery, when he reached Liverpool in 1873. At a waterfront tavern in Paradise Street, he told a motley crew of associates that he had been woken up in the hold of the *Marie Celeste* to the sound of an ominous, deafening rumble. Apparently, it was caused by the alcohol in the barrels, fermenting in the sweltering tropical heat.

He was convinced that an explosion was imminent, so he was forced to break his cover and scramble hurriedly up on deck. To his total bewilderment, there was no one there. All the crew had abandoned ship and were huddled together in the only lifeboat, which was attached to the ship by a long line of around 300 yards. Foyle quickly realised that they had also been frightened of the unstable cargo and had consequently put as much distance between themselves and the ship as possible, by taking refuge in the lifeboat.

Foyle repeatedly pleaded with them to allow him on to the boat, but they refused, so he angrily grabbed an axe and severed the tow rope. The lifeboat carrying the crew drifted off towards the horizon and Foyle fell to his knees and prayed for salvation. Inexplicably, the cargo gradually stabilised and the danger subsided. When Captain Moorhouse, who found the ship, was towing the *Marie Celeste* into the harbour at Gibraltar, he saw Foyle come out on deck. Potentially, he could have ruined the salvage prize, so Moorhouse let him go. This account all ties in with the established facts. At the court of enquiry, witnesses stated that an unaccounted-for crew member left the *Dei Gratia* and set out for England. Mystery solved?

I recently uncovered an article in an old newspaper which may throw some light on the fate of the *Marie Celeste's* crew. On 16 May 1873, the *Daily Albion* of Liverpool reported that fishermen at Baudus, in Asturias, near Madrid, had spotted two rafts floating in the Atlantic coastal waters off the Spanish mainland. One of the rafts had a corpse lashed to its side and was flying an American flag. The second raft carried five decomposing bodies. For some unaccountable reason, the reports were never fully looked into, so we will never know from which ship the dead bodies originated. Could they possibly have been from the *Marie Celeste*?

Sentimental Journey

B illy Marston had a very special knack for remembering things in great detail, because his work demanded it. A considerable part of his job as a painter and decorator was to work out estimates, and to then recall what materials would be required, and in what quantities and measurements, without the need to even note them down.

Billy remembers the date of the following strange incident quite clearly, in every detail, even though he was eighty-nine when he related his account of it to me.

It was Monday, 11 November 1974. Every newspaper, every radio and television news programme was full of the mysterious disappearance of the Earl of Lucan. The vanishing lord had abandoned the car he had used to flee from London at Newhaven on the south coast. Detectives had hoped to catch up with the Earl to determine whether he could help them with their inquiries into the 'Upstairs-Downstairs' murder of the Lucan children's nanny, and the attack on Lady Lucan.

The elusive Lord Lucan has still not been found to this day. Much was made of his vanishing act in the media at the time, and he became quite a household name.

As one mystery unfolded in London on that rainy November night, another one was about to commence two hundred miles further north in the Mossley Hill area of Liverpool.

At around 9pm, at a public house on Rose Lane called the Rose of Mossley, sixty-year-old bachelor Billy Marston, was lost in thought as he leaned at the bar, his cloth-capped head bowed over a half-empty glass of Mackeson stout. Billy was inwardly reminiscing about the past and, at the same time, worrying about the future. A painter and decorator by trade, Billy was increasingly finding that much younger men were being employed in the painting and decorating business and he was finding it hard to compete. Anyway, it wouldn't be long before he was drawing his old age pension. Where had all those years gone? What had happened to all his friends and relatives?

Once upon a time, many years ago, he used to go out on dates with attractive women, and had lots of friends and brothers and sisters. But, sadly, he was now the sole survivor of his family and most of his friends had gone away to other areas, lost touch with him, or died. His best friend Mulhearne had died suddenly a year ago from heart failure. It had been a terrible shock and made him feel old. Julia, the sister who had been closest to Billy since childhood, had died from cancer five years before that.

With a deep sigh, Billy drank the last dregs of his glass of stout, and said goodnight to the barman. He left the pub and wearily trudged down Rose Lane towards his home, the way he did most nights, back to his lonely and rather neglected house on Woodlands Road.

As Billy trudged along through the soft drizzle, a gloomy depression engulfed him as he contemplated the bleakness of his life. He began to wallow in self-pity, and felt his throat choking up with melancholy, when a man came walking out of a side street and startled him. In a low, professional-sounding singing voice the stranger sang a song which Billy hadn't heard for years. The song was Sentimental Journey and dated back to the 1940s. The first verse floated through the damp night air:

> *Gonna take a sentimental journey,*
> *Gonna set my heart at ease,*
> *Gonna make a sentimental journey*
> *To renew old memories.*

The stranger's youthful stride quickly put increasing distance between himself and Billy Marston, and in less than a minute, he was a fleeting figure, barely visible through the drizzle as he flitted up the lane. He could still be heard whistling the wistful melody as he melted into the shadows of a large oak tree's overhanging branches.

Billy slowed down, the words still ringing in his ears. He knew the song well and it had struck a chord in him.

"That sounds like a good idea," he muttered to himself, "I think I'll take a sentimental journey of my own."

His mood immediately lifted. He turned, and walked off in the opposite direction with a renewed sense of purpose. He had decided to revisit his old neighbourhood on Penny Lane. He was filled with the need to go on a sort of pilgrimage, to pay some homage to the golden years of his life. There are mental states of heightened alertness in the human mind of which we are hardly aware. The alpha, beta, delta rhythms of the mind as it sleeps, pays attention, or meditates, are fairly well known to neurologists, but this state of heightened consciousness was completely alien to Billy. It was almost euphoric, yet mystical.

As Billy reached the corner of Briardale Road and Penny Lane, he turned right, and as he did so, he made a turning back into into the world of 1929. The drizzle was suddenly no more and Billy felt as if he was fifteen again. Stiff joints, rheumatic twinges and eyes blurred by cataracts were no more, he felt sprightly, energised and fully alive. And bliss! The teeth in his mouth were his own again. The cloth cap had inexplicably vanished from his bald pate, to reveal a head of thick blonde hair.

He immediately noticed that the shops on the lane were the ones that had been there in the 1920s. The shops had all shut up for the night, but he noted all the old, familiar painted signs above their fronts. The old greengrocers, the bread and cake shop, the newsagent and tobacconist. Mrs Bruce, one of his aunt's neighbours, came down the lane. As she shuffled past him, she said, "You'd best be getting home, Billy. You young gallivanter."

Billy gazed at her in awe, but felt impelled to walk on, for he instinctively knew that if he was to allow himself to doubt that he was back in the late 1920s, for even one second, the spell would be broken and he'd find himself back on the rainy night-time street of 1974.

He walked on as if in a dream. The distinctive low moaning sound of a rolling tramcar brought a smile of recognition to Billy's face. It sailed into his view, rocking slowly from side to side up Smithdown Road: a tram with a ghostly, gas-lit interior. Shadowy figures were both seated and standing in its saloon, heading for the terminus. Cobbled roads stretched before him where macadam surfaces had lain in the dreary decade he'd left behind.

He crossed the road, hopping over tram lines worn shiny by a non-stop stream of trams ferrying their passengers to and from the city centre, and made his way to the home of his youth on Charles Berrington Road. He unbuttoned his overcoat and removed his scarf; it was a lovely warm evening and felt like summer. Downwind, on a gentle breeze, came the delightful, memory-jogging aroma of Ogden's mellow pipe tobacco. Two old men, Mr Godley and the meerschaum pipe-smoking Mr Greene, stood on their neighbouring doorsteps chatting, or 'chinwagging', as they used to call it back in the twenties. They were discussing Lancashire's recent win by ten wickets against South Africa at the three-day match at Liverpool Cricket Club, in Aigburth. Billy noted everything they said as he passed by.

Further up the road he passed old Mrs Brown's front parlour window and heard her playing a truly haunting melody on her old upright piano. It was Hoagy Carmichael's Stardust. In 1929 Billy had courted a beautiful girl named Violet who had loved that song. Filled with nostalgia, the music tugged at his heartstrings and he felt the full force of the emotions he had experienced at the time. He resolved to call at her home in a short while, just to hold her in his arms one more time.

Billy gazed up at the jewelled, velvety sky and whispered a few very apt lines which he had remembered from the song Mrs Brown was gently playing:

> *High up in the sky the little stars climb,*
> *Always reminding me that we're apart,*
> *You wandered down the lane and far away,*
> *Leaving me a song that will not die.*

A red-nosed drunk with a rakishly tilted bowler hat embraced the column of a lamp-post as he howled out Old Man River – shattering Billy's reveries about the stars and Violet and romance.

Billy paused as he approached the bay window of the front parlour he knew so well from long ago; the front parlour of his own old house, where he had lived until he was married at the age of twenty-two. An overwhelming sadness and emptiness suddenly came over him, damping down the euphoric rush that had so far accompanied his sojourn into the past. His poor, working-class mother and father and sisters lived at the house, and they had barely been able to scrape together a living in those hard times. Billy wished he could somehow convert all of his savings in 1974 into the currency of 1929 and stuff it through the letterbox in the front door. But that would only create a paradox.

Billy stood in the shadows, gazing at the house, afraid to knock on the front door he knew so well. He knew that if he entered that house, he would never be able to leave again. It would simply be too emotional to pay a flying visit, and something deep down told him that this stroll into bygone days was due to come to an end at any moment.

Then, suddenly, the front door opened.

Billy's heart thumped wildly inside his chest. His mother leant down and put the empty milk bottles out on the step. The family's old, one-eyed cat, Nelson, brushed past her legs and sauntered out into the street. The cat arched his back when he caught sight of Billy's stock-still silhouette lurking outside the lamp-post's fringe of illumination.

"Mum…" the faint word barely escaped from Billy's choked-up throat and drifted into the night air unheard by his beloved mother.

The door closed and Billy heard the sound of a bolt being drawn inside. He looked down at his old cat and bent down to reach out to him saying, "Nelson. Here, puss. Do you know who I am?"

The cat hissed and ran off into the night.

Billy silently said goodbye to the house and reluctantly walked away with scalding tears cascading down his cheeks. He stopped on Heathfield Road, and once again, his emotions were in turmoil. He stared at the upstairs window of Violet's bedroom. He knew that his first love was sleeping there, unaware of everything. The thought of tossing a handful of gravel at the window crossed his mind, but he knew that he had no right to confuse her – he must leave her be.

A policeman was approaching on his beat along Smithdown Road. It was time to leave.

"I will always love you, Violet," Billy whispered, eyeing the drawn curtains behind which his eternal sweetheart lay sleeping. He could almost hear her singing the words of Stardust in his mind.

Violet would die from a brain tumour in three years time …

Billy sorrowfully retraced his steps back up Penny Lane, until he reached the corner where his amazing journey into the past had begun. He knew that he couldn't stay in the past, and silently accepted the fact without protest. He was too upset to object. Whenever he had reminisced publicly about the good old days, people had told him he'd been looking at the past through rose-tinted spectacles, but now he knew that he hadn't. Now he knew exactly what he had lost – those carefree, halcyon days when his greatest worry had been what to wear on his dates with his sweetheart, Violet.

As Billy walked up Briardale Road, the stiffness of old age gradually returned to his joints and limbs, rheumatism became evident once again in his shoulder, and his vision clouded over once more, as the cataracts covered his eyes. A modern car sped past, then another – gone were the virtually car-free streets of the 1920s. He had returned to 1974 and the noise and bustle of the busy streets around Penny Lane made him feel dizzy and confused.

When Billy arrived home he sat in silence for a while, going over and over the night's events in his head. He could not be sure that he wasn't going mad.

How on earth, and for what reason, had he been allowed to go back over forty years to the 1920s? It was a question to which he never found the answer.

On the following morning, right out of the blue, Billy was visited by a cousin with whom he'd lost touch, called Andy. Andy had travelled from St Helens specifically to find Billy, and admitted that his motivation for seeking him out had been loneliness, because he no longer had any immediate family around him. They had all died, one by one, leaving Andy completely on his own in the world. He had then remembered his cousin who was about the same age as himself.

Perhaps because they were both in the same situation, Billy and Andy got on famously and chatted into the small hours about incidents from their childhood and early lives. Here was a real life link with the past, thought Billy. It turned out that they still had a great deal in common; so much so, in fact, that Billy soon invited his cousin to live with him, and they made a pact to create and build a proper social life for themselves.

They started by paying a visit to the local crown green bowling club. Not only did they both enjoy the game and find that they were good at it, but they also met two women who took them off to ballroom dancing classes. Lonely nights and self-imposed isolation became a thing of the past for the two cousins and suddenly their old age did not seem so bleak after all. As an added bonus, all the exercise seemed to help Billy's rheumatism, and his painful, creaking joints eased.

Shortly after relating his touching timeslip tale to me, Billy Marston passed away, aged eighty-nine. He struck me as a very honest and straightforward man, and he earnestly assured me that the trip into the past really did take place, but he was at a loss to explain why or how it happened. What is apparent is that that night appeared to be a turning point in Billy's life, and from that time onward, he seemed to find his way again.

A Dance with Death

In the summer of 1885, a small slender woman with a pale childish face visited Liverpool. She was twenty-nine-year-old Elizabeth Berry of Oldham, and she had come to the city to visit a relative who lived on Duke Street. After the visit, Elizabeth journeyed across the Mersey on the ferry to see a cousin over at New Brighton, and ended up staying at the seaside resort for three days. On the last day of her visit, Elizabeth entered the tent of the expensive and controversial fortune-teller, Madame Rosamund, who had intrigued her since the day she arrived. Rosamund, who claimed to be of Romany descent, broke the golden rule of fortune telling: never reveal the details of a forthcoming death to a client.

"You have had many deaths in your life – Elizabeth," said Rosamund in a strange-sounding low voice, as she peered knowingly into the dark glassy depths of a purple-tinted crystal ball.

"Yes, yes, I have," Elizabeth replied, then queried: "But how do you know my name?"

"Your husband gone ... your son gone ..." Madame Rosamund whispered.

A shiver of apprehension shot down Elizabeth's spine. What the fortune-teller said was true. Four years ago, Elizabeth's invalid husband, Thomas, had died suddenly, and just over a year later, their son had also passed away. At the time of his death he had been sleeping in a damp bed in Blackpool. Elizabeth had received the sum of seventy pounds from an insurance policy when her husband died, and five pounds for the death of her son.

"Oh! The shadow is reaching out now for your daughter ..." said Rosamund enigmatically, looking at her terrified client from under her jet black lashes.

Rosamund's large dark eyes widened and probed deeper into the very nucleus of the crystal sphere. Elizabeth felt faint at the shocking news, but there was another terrible revelation still to come. Oblivious to Elizabeth's evident distress, Rosamund continued to reel off what lay in store for the young widow in the future.

"You will dance with a tall dark stranger, and he will drop you and take your life. His eyes are brown – they twinkle like the stars – and he will captivate you, but he will surely kill you. His eyes will be full of tears when he sees what he has done. You will then go to the terrible place of darkness and gnashing of teeth."

Trembling, Elizabeth stood up, and backed away from the sinister fortune teller. The unrepentant Madame Rosamund covered the crystal ball with a dark green velvet cloth and gently shook her head, "I only read the future, my dear, warts and all."

Some time later, Elizabeth was invited to a ball in Oldham by her local butcher, thirty-five-year-old Tom Whittaker. Elizabeth politely declined the invitation, concerned lest Whittaker should turn out to be the tall dark man with the twinkling brown eyes who would kill her. He was certainly tall and dark-eyed, and Elizabeth had often winced at the way the young butcher would hack the blood-drained carcasses with his enormous meat cleaver. She shuddered at the recollection. No! She would rather stay at home with her knitting, thank you very much!

A month after that, old Mr Hargreaves, the counter clerk from the local post office, invited the pretty young widow to a soirée at the local church hall. Mr Hargreaves was bald and blue-eyed, so there was no way he could be the brown-eyed killer foretold by the fortune-teller, and she accepted his invitation, thinking it would make a pleasant, if rather unexciting, change.

So Elizabeth Berry walked hand in hand with a man old enough to be her father into a church hall one hot July night in 1885. The two of them joined in the dancing, until, at one point in the evening, Mr Hargreaves sat down to rest his weary legs, leaving Elizabeth on the periphery of the dance floor, still eager to join in the dancing. She made a very pretty picture, with her black curly hair tied up with a silk crimson bow, and her ivory white dress prettily adorned with pearls and pink roses. Her round face was childish, and being powdered and flushed from all the dancing, she didn't look a day over sixteen.

She did not have to wait long before a tall man with hair as black and curly as Elizabeth's own approached her. He invited her to dance, but she shook her head and cast her eyes down, nervously.

Death had arrived.

"Oh, come now, don't be such a wallflower," teased the man in a deep voice, betraying an American accent.

Without waiting for a reply, the tall dark stranger grabbed her hand and Elizabeth felt dizzy and faint. She almost fell towards him. Her heart was palpitating. She was a helpless doll in his muscular arms, and he waltzed wildly with her across the dance floor. Everything was swirling. The chandelier swam by overhead, and the other couples spun past like mad dervishes. The American's cologne was masculine and as overpowering as he himself was. The heady aroma stifled her, yet Elizabeth Berry had never felt more alive in all of her twenty-nine years.

When the musicians stopped playing and the waltz ended, Elizabeth and the American were out of breath, and both were obviously filled with lust for one another. Growing increasingly agitated, Mr Hargreaves had been watching all these goings on from the sidelines and at the earliest opportunity he grabbed Elizabeth's arm, upon which the American, a Texan whose name was Brett, said, "Sir, may I compliment you? Your daughter is truly the finest English Rose I have set eyes upon since coming to this country."

Hargreaves ample cheeks puffed with fury, and in no uncertain terms, he told Brett that he was not Elizabeth's father, but a good friend. Two other men who had been eyeing Elizabeth Berry with lecherous desire, seized their opportunity and they confronted the American and accused him of insulting a senior citizen of Oldham. A serious fight ensued, and Hargreaves and another man bundled Elizabeth Berry out of the church hall and took her home. At her gate, Hargreaves made a pass at Elizabeth, but she laughingly told him that she was not interested in him in a physical way, merely as a friend. When Hargreaves heard the bare, unpalatable truth, he surprised her by bursting into tears, then sucking his thumb!

That night, Elizabeth lay awake in her bed, thinking constantly of Brett's wide manly shoulders, his sleek black hair, and those dark penetrating brown eyes. She was so totally smitten that she convinced herself that Madame Rosamund had lied to her – the handsome American couldn't possibly do her any harm.

The summer mellowed as the weeks passed, and in the late August of 1885, a young local policeman named Bob Oakley invited Elizabeth to another ball, this time in Manchester. The ball had been organised by the Manchester Police Force, and most of the people attending the occasion were either policemen, ex-policemen, or their relatives. Young Oakley never danced once with Elizabeth Berry, as he didn't get a chance. She had created quite a stir, and the hot-blooded police constables crowded about her and queued up to take her in their arms and sweep her across the dance floor.

Of all the men who waylaid her that evening, only one caught the eye and heart of Elizabeth, and his name was James. He was tall, with hair as black as coal, and eyes of smouldering lignite brown. They flashed with emotion as James twirled her effortlessly around the dance floor. Elizabeth sat at a table with James and found him to be the most perfect, courteous, gallant and handsome man she had ever set eyes upon. She told him about her bereavements, and how she hoped to rebuild a life for herself and her daughter and become a nurse at the Oldham Workhouse, but when Elizabeth tried to discover if James was a policeman, he steered the conversation away in another direction. All Elizabeth was able to ascertain from the conversation was that James was a bachelor. Anyway, whatever his occupation, she argued to herself, he was obviously a kind and caring man. Yet again, although James matched perfectly Rosamund's description of Elizabeth's future killer, her emotions were powerful enough to blot out the fortune teller's awful predictions.

Then came a most curious coincidence. James learned that Elizabeth's surname was the same as his – Berry. If they married, James mused, Elizabeth would still retain her original surname. All this talk of marriage gave Elizabeth the courage to hint that perhaps they should keep in touch, but James Berry sighed and told her that his work would be taking him to another town, faraway, in the morning. After that, he was needed in another part of the country, and such was the itinerant nature of his job, that he was rarely in one place for more than a day at a time.

That night, James guided Elizabeth out on to a balcony, as every other couple savoured the last waltz. They clung to each other and kissed passionately by the light of the full moon, as the last strains of the music filled their ears. James said he knew in his soul that he would meet Elizabeth again one day, and when that day came, he would give up his work and marry her. They both cried on the balcony beneath the moon and stars. But, within half an hour, James was travelling east, and Elizabeth was travelling west back to Oldham.

Elizabeth Berry worked for a while as a nurse at the Oldham Workhouse, but she did not really enjoy the work, and inwardly believed that she deserved a better station in life. Her annual salary was just twenty-five pounds, and that was not nearly enough to pay for good clothes and a decent lifestyle. Elizabeth had a strange dual personality, and she would be kindness itself to the patients one day, and cruel and heartless to them the next. There were also strange rumours circulating about the daughter Elizabeth Berry hardly mentioned. This was eleven-year-old Edith Annie Berry, whom she had placed in the care of an aunt.

In January 1887, Elizabeth invited the child back into her life, but unfortunately, the girl fell gravely ill within days of the reunion. Elizabeth Berry's neighbours, who had no doubt already decided that she was a bit of a flighty piece, because of all her admirers, whispered that the widow was cursed, but others attributed Edith Annie's illness to a rather more sinister cause. After all, it was widely known that Edith's mother had recently taken out an insurance policy on her daughter, and stood to receive ten pounds compensation if the girl should die. This was true – however, Elizabeth Berry had also taken out a second policy that would pay out one hundred pounds to either Edith or her mother, depending on who lived the longer.

Little Edith Annie died in agony at five o'clock in the morning on the day after she had fallen ill. Given that Elizabeth Berry had now lost a husband, a son and a daughter to mysterious illnesses, and had received insurance payouts in each case, foul play was suspected. A Dr Patterson and several other doctors performed a post-mortem on Edith Annie – and discovered a powerful poison – possibly sulphuric acid – both in her stomach and in samples of her vomit.

Several people who had known Elizabeth came forward and expressed their belief that she had even murdered her own mother with poison, as she had died in similar circumstances. So Elizabeth's mother was duly exhumed – and poison was indeed found in her stomach. Other former friends added to the case for the prosecution, claiming that Elizabeth not only smoked opium, but was an immoral flirt who read sensational lurid novels. All Elizabeth Berry could say in her defence was that if, as the prosecution claimed, she had poisoned her mother, husband and children, then she must have been insane at the time.

However, her pleas of insanity went unheeded and she was tried, found guilty and sentenced to death for the murder of her mother by poisoning. A second case – that she had murdered Edith Annie – was not brought before the courts. The date set for her execution was Monday, 14 March 1887, and the place was Kirkdale Prison.

That fateful day soon arrived, and hundreds of Liverpudlians who had eagerly read the lurid accounts of the dreadful poisonings, braved the snow and icy winds as they gathered at the foot of the prison walls. Immediately prior to the execution, the hangman visited Elizabeth in her cell. She looked up as he entered and realised at once that it was James Berry, the man she had danced with two years before. When they saw one another, they stood motionless, both of them in shock. The prison warders glanced back and forth between Elizabeth and James, until one of them said, "Have you met before?"

James Berry nodded, and asked if he could spend a few private moments alone with the condemned woman.

"Of course," said the senior warder. "Knock when you want us to collect her."

The hangman and the murderess embraced in the cold dark cell, and both faintly sobbed. Madame Rosamund's prophecy had come to pass ... You will dance with a tall dark stranger, and he will drop you and take your life. His eyes are brown, they twinkle like the stars, and he will captivate you, but he will surely kill you. His eyes will be full of tears when he sees what he has done ...

James assured Elizabeth that her death would be quick and painless. He would make sure of that in the positioning of the knot around her beautiful, delicate neck.

Outside in the prison yard, warders were sprinkling sand over the snowy path to the gallows, to make sure that Elizabeth would not slip. Meanwhile, in the cell, the hangman was saying, "I never forgot you in those two years, Elizabeth. No woman has eyes as beautiful as yours. No woman on this earth has touched my heart the way that you did that moonlit summer night."

The hands of the prison clock ticked relentlessly on, and soon the warders grew impatient. They knocked on the cell door and asked James Berry if he was ready. In a choked voice, he replied that he was. The chaplain accompanied Elizabeth and the warders and the executioner to the gallows. James Berry climbed up first and readied himself for the dreadful task that lay ahead. He glanced down and saw that Elizabeth had fainted. Two warders carried her up to the scaffold, and she was positioned over the trapdoor – or 'the drop', as it was known.

As James Berry pinioned her feet together and adjusted the straps, Elizabeth regained consciousness, and gasped in horror as the heavy noose was adjusted around her neck.

"May the Lord have mercy upon me," she whispered. "Lord receive my spirit."

The white hood was gently placed over her head, and she kissed the hangman's hand as he pulled the cloth over her soft face. The chaplain prayed in a low muttering voice, and James Berry closed his eyes as he threw the lever which drew the bolt. In an instant, the trapdoor sprang open and Elizabeth Berry plunged into eternity.

James Berry would later voluntarily retire from his grisly occupation and openly condemned capital punishment as an obscene abomination. People often asked him why he had abandoned and attacked his own profession in such a way, and Berry would always refuse to give a satisfactory explanation, but I'm sure that Elizabeth's death was the sole reason.

THE BOOKIES' NIGHTMARE

It is a common belief in occult lore that no one should make monetary gain out of his or her psychic powers. Indeed, many genuine 'sensitives' consider that, as their faculty is a gift from God, it would be downright immoral to abuse their talent for material gain. Some psychics believe that such misuse of their supernatural powers would automatically result in their gift being irreversibly removed or, worse still, could end in death or tragedy. However, there are many cases of people using information of a future event, glimpsed during a premonition, to acquire wealth, without any resulting ill-effects.

In 1967, an Everton man, named Freddie McKiver, had a blazing row with his wife and walked out to live with his sister, Joan, for a week to cool down. Joan lived alone in Pendennis Street, near Cabbage Hall and had a spare room which she never used and was quite happy to put her brother up. In this room there was an old bed, which had belonged to the previous occupier. It smelt a bit musky, but Freddie McKiver decided that it had to be better than sleeping on the cramped, two-seater settee in the living room.

On the first night he slept in that bed, Freddie McKiver dreamed that he saw two horses winning a race at Newmarket. In the dream, someone shouted out the horses' names. The next day he went into the bookmakers – Bernard Murphy and Sons – and put a few bob on both horses. Each won its race, making McKiver a very happy man.

On the following night, he was asleep in bed again, when he dreamed that he saw not two, but three horses winning races at various meetings. He was even able to read the names of the horses on the racing page of the newspaper. He was so convinced that he was on a winning streak, that he borrowed money from Joan and placed bets on all three. Each horse came in first and netted McKiver a substantial sum of money.

Armed with a bunch of flowers and a box of chocolates, McKiver decided that it was about time that he returned to his wife and he told her all about the weird but lucrative dreams. That night he did not dream about horses at all. Indeed, after he woke up, he could not even remember having dreamt of anything at all. He wondered if the phenomenon was connected in some way to the old bed in his sister's house. Perhaps it was somehow lucky. He offered his sister money for the old smelly bed but she was only too glad to be rid of it and told him that he could have it for nothing. He took it over to his house in Heyworth Street and installed it in the spare room.

That night he slept alone in the bed, because his wife felt nauseated by the odour that the mattress gave off. He dreamed he could see the name of the horse that would win the 1.30 at Plumpton. He was particularly excited because the horse's odds were 33-1. The next day, McKiver put as much money as he could muster on the horse and created a furore at the bookmakers, but they honoured the bet and paid out hundreds of pounds when the horse won.

When McKiver returned home, after enjoying a celebratory pub crawl, his wife angrily informed him that she had found cockroaches in the spare room, which must have come from the old bed and she had got the children to take it into the alleyway. In a panic, he dashed round to the back of the house where, to his horror, he found the charred remains of the old bed – a mere skeleton of blackened springs. Freddie McKiver's suspicions that the bed was the source of his good luck were confirmed and he never had another lucrative dream.

Someone else who gave the bookies sleepless nights because of his psychic talents, was Lord Kilbracken. In March 1946, he dreamt that he could read the entire racing results of the following Saturday evening's paper and he distinctly noticed that two horses, named Bindal and Juladin, had won races at starting prices of 7-1. He backed both horses when he woke up the next day and also tipped off friends. The dream came true and netted Kilbracken and his associates a considerable fortune. Unfortunately, after successfully predicting that Mr What would win the 1958 Grand National at Aintree, the Lord's precognitive faculty deserted him just as suddenly and mysteriously as it had arrived, never to return.

NIGHT TERRORS

There is a type of ghost which is particularly frightening because it does not haunt houses, but people. Such tormenting phantoms often manifest themselves out of the blue for no apparent reason and then haunt a person, sometimes daily, as regularly as clockwork, or alternatively intermittently over the space of many years, and no matter where the person goes, the entity follows.

In 1981, a horror film called *The Entity* was released, which featured just such a person-centred haunting. The demonic entity featured in the movie actually raped a woman and victimised her repeatedly, no matter where she went. The film was based upon the well-documented case of a woman in Culver City, California, who was repeatedly raped with the utmost violence in her own home by a sinister supernatural force (interpreted as a demon) which followed her about, even after she had moved five times.

Closer to home, here in Liverpool, there have been similar cases reported from the Victorian era to the present day. Here is a letter from a woman who asked me not to divulge her real name:

Dear Tom,

From 1997 to the present day, my daughter and I have been persecuted by something terrifying that invades our beds after dark. I hope you will believe me and hopefully advise me on ridding my home of these evil entities. In May 1997 I was living in the Croxteth area of Liverpool with my daughter, then aged 15. I had been separated from my husband since 1994. On May 31, 1997, which I remember being a Saturday night, I went to bed around half-past twelve. My daughter had already gone to bed at 10.30pm.

Around one in the morning, I felt something sit down on the edge of my bed, near the bottom. It was so heavy I thought a burglar was sitting on the bed, and was so terrified, I just pretended I was asleep. I then felt something cold get into the bed with me and lay beside me. I knew it was something supernatural by the way it got into the bed without lifting the duvet, in such a fast way. I turned away from this thing and it somehow slid over me, like a snake almost. For a brief moment I opened my eyes, and saw the most terrifying face on my pillow, facing me. I shouted, "Go away!" but then this thing had its way with me – actually had intercourse with me.

When it left the bed I jumped up, turned on the bedroom light, ran into the hallway, switched on the light there, then did the same in the lounge, where I tried to smoke a cigarette as I cried.

This lady's letter then went on to describe how her daughter reported the same experience with what seems to have been the same entity. Mother and daughter assumed the house, which was rather old, was haunted by something truly evil and eventually moved to a more modern house in Old Swan, hoping that that would be an end to their problems.

For the first few weeks the mother and her teenaged daughter slept uneasily, fearful of the return of the chilling night visitor, but they eventually started to relax. Then, in the January of 1998, the thing – whatever it was – did return. The mother was lying in her bed with the radio tuned to Radio 2, when she realised that something was turning the volume down. The room was plunged into silence – then came a faint sniggering sound. The bed began to rock gently, and she realised with utter dread that the night terror had returned to abuse her. Its cold bony hand slid up her back, and it started to cackle. She jumped out of bed, threw back the curtains, and turned to be confronted by a hideous, misshapen, skeletal black creature of some sort with a small round head and staring black-rimmed eyes.

In a state of pure terror the victim turned on her sinister persecutor and repeatedly swore at it. The thing hissed back at her like an angry snake, then slithered off the bed into the darkness. The bedroom door, which was ajar, moved slightly, as if the thing had brushed against it on its way out, and then followed the patter of footsteps rapidly ascending the stairs – up to the room where her daughter lay sleeping. Less than a few seconds later, as the mother was fetching a large carving knife from the kitchen, she heard her daughter let out a bloodcurdling scream, followed by a succession of bumps and thumps, and the sound of demonic laughing.

The mother raced up the stairs to find her daughter coming towards her sobbing hysterically, and they both ended up barricading themselves in the living room until the break of dawn.

In desperation to be rid of their malign intruder, the mother and daughter moved once more, this time to Aigburth, but the thing turned up there as well one night, when the daughter awoke to find it crawling along on its belly towards her bed from the corner of the room.

The mother and daughter told one parapsychologist about these continual nocturnal invasions by the entity, and he advised them to seek counselling from a psychotherapist, or psychiatrist. I knew better, having read and investigated many reports of Old Hag Syndrome and succubus and incubus attacks over the many years I had spent studying this phenomenon.

The first rule about tackling these demons of the night is to try not to fear them – obviously easier said than done – but they thrive on the fear which they generate in their victims. The advice I give to those who are subjected to these attacks is that they should close their eyes if they are faced with hideous apparitions and try and shut them out. Then the God the victim believes in should be invoked to combat the entity. Even seasoned atheists will quickly call upon a higher power when they experience Old Hag, or any type of night terror visitations. Lights should always be left on, near to, or better still, in the actual room where the attacks take place, because these things that prey on people detest light – another argument which supports their possible demonic origins. Keeping a Bible in the room where the attacks take place is also a good idea, and perhaps a crucifix. As an extreme measure, the house should be blessed by a priest.

When the mother and daughter in question followed this advice, the malevolent entity finally stopped visiting them, and at the time of writing, it has failed to put in any further appearances at the mother's home. The daughter is in her early twenties now and lives close to her mother. She too has experienced nothing out the ordinary since her home was blessed, but she always sleeps with a nightlight on these days and keeps a copy of the Bible at the side of her bed – just in case!

BRIDEGROOM REVISITED

In the year 1870, a twenty-year-old man from Ormskirk named John Hargreaves was picnicking with his cousin in the Lake District, near Kendal. The awe-inspiring pastoral scenery which spread before him took his breath away. His attention was suddenly diverted when a beautiful girl, aged about sixteen or seventeen, caught his eye. Her name was Sarah Parr, the youngest daughter of a local farmer who had recently fallen on hard times. That evening, after Hargreaves' persistent pestering, the country girl was introduced to him by his cousin. John was so mesmerised by her beauty, that he decided to stay at his cousin's cottage for the remainder of the summer, just so that he could spend time with Sarah.

Very soon a loving relationship blossomed between the innocent pair. However, the sweet romance was dramatically catapulted back into reality at the end of July, when Sarah informed John Hargreaves that she was carrying his child. At first, the couple were elated, but John's father, a wealthy landowner, was furious when he heard the news. He issued his son with the ultimatum that if he married Sarah Parr, he would be excluded from his will and his monthly allowance would be stopped immediately. It seemed that John Hargreaves senior had plans for his son to marry the daughter of a wealthy Liverpool shipwright instead.

John thought long and hard and then made a decision. He ignored his heart and chose monetary gain over the love of his sweetheart. That evening, he took Sarah for a walk to one of their favourite haunts, a rocky ledge above a fast-flowing stream which came straight off the fells. In this beautiful spot, he coldly announced to her that he was returning to Ormskirk, and that he would be doing so without her. Naturally, Sarah was devastgated by the news and became hysterical, pleading with her callous lover to reconsider. She screamed pitifully for him to return, but he steeled himself to ignore her, for he was nearly as distressed as she was, but he walked on nevertheless, until he heard her shriek, "I will haunt you until your dying day!" At this dramatic claim, Hargreaves glanced around just in time to see the desperate girl leap from the rocky ledge into the boulder-strewn stream below. The brutal tumble broke her delicate neck, and it is said that the entire stream turned red with her blood.

Just one year later, Hargreaves was at the altar, marrying the prestigious Mary Holt, some accounts say it was St Oswald's Church, near Rufford. During the ceremony, when the priest asked if anyone present objected to the union of John Hargreaves and Mary Holt, members of the congregation were aware of the persistent sound of a baby crying somewhere nearby, yet no one could actually see a baby in the church. Then, gradually, a dark shadow materialised behind the kneeling couple, in the middle of the aisle. People seated at the front said it looked like the ghost of a frail girl. The mysterious figure wore a black veil which covered a chalk-white face. She seemed to be dressed all in black and was clutching a crying baby in her arms.

John Hargreaves immediately seemed to recognise the gloomy spectre and his face paled and he began to tremble. He was so terrified that he ran straight out of the church, causing the marriage service to be abandoned. At the same time, the congregation was shocked to see that the girl in black and her baby had also vanished, leaving no trace. The number of witnesses to this strange event was astonishing. About one hundred and thirty people claimed to have seen the ghostly lady.

Only one week later, John Hargreaves was found dead in his bed with a frozen look of absolute terror etched on his face. A servant claimed to have heard him screaming out at four o'clock that morning. Apparently the distraught man had been repeatedly shouting, "Leave me alone! Please, leave me alone!"

SPEKE POLTERGEIST

HAUNTED LIVERPOOL 4

A few years ago there was a spate of poltergeist activity centred around a teenager called Alice who lived in Speke. At first, the family thought that their house was haunted and they decided to move elsewhere. But the poltergeist followed them and it actually started knocking and tapping on the roof and windscreen of the removal van and even cracked the nearside mirror. The funniest, yet also the most alarming incident, took place as the girl was playing football in their new garden. The poltergeist somehow managed to pull off her underwear, without removing her outer clothes. The girl was naturally shocked and screamed as first her bra and then her briefs fluttered about in the air, before landing on their new neighbour's clothes line.

I went along to investigate the phenomena with two other people and we actually witnessed the poltergeist activity in the kitchen of the girl's home. Knives, pots and pans flew about all over the place and an unplugged electric kettle started to boil furiously without anyone having turned it on. One of the investigators actually taped the sounds in the room. On the recording there is the voice of a man, groaning loudly, yet no one present remembered hearing this voice at the time. The poltergeist then turned nasty and what I can only describe as a very strong cold gust of air engulfed the three of us. The other two ghost investigators turned and fled in panic, but I stayed put and something strong pushed against my chest, almost knocking me over.

At this point, Alice's mother stepped forward to help me and a long carving knife flew through the air, straight towards her. It missed her by millimetres and finished up embedded in the door of the gas meter cupboard in the hall. Then, just as suddenly as it had begun, all the activity ceased and the house fell silent. Afterwards, all the cutlery and pots and pans in the kitchen were found to have been magnetised during the incident. After that day, the poltergeist was only active for one more brief period and thankfully, it has been uneasily quiet in the house ever since.

THE LIGHTHOUSE GHOUL

HAUNTED LIVERPOOL 1

Perch Rock is a large outcrop of red sandstone which juts out into the River Mersey from the northern tip of the Wirral Peninsula. The cliffs that line the coast from Perch Rock to the Dee Estuary, are known to be riddled with tunnels and caverns that were once used by smugglers and there are many fascinating old tales about this stretch of coastline; but the following story is not about contraband, it is about murder and the supernatural ...

In the summer of 1827, the foundation stone of the New Brighton Lighthouse was laid in the middle of Perch Rock by the Liverpool Dock Trustees. Granite was brought from Anglesey and volcanic cement from the slopes of Mount Etna for the foundation of the lighthouse, which was opened in March 1830. The tower stood 90 feet high and the powerful beam of its light was soon sweeping Liverpool Bay to guide ships on their voyages.

The first keeper, an elderly man named Garratt, died unexpectedly at the lighthouse one night and was quickly replaced by a sixty-five-year-old, ex-sea captain from Wallasey, Jack Maudley. Maudley was regarded as an odd character by those who knew him. He was a loner which made him eminently suitable for the job and he had a black cat which he took everywhere with him. Maudley wrote to his brother in Liverpool telling him about his new job, saying that he would enjoy the isolation on Perch Rock where he would be far removed from the wagging tongues of his neighbourhood. Maudley was referring to the (not entirely unfounded) rumours of him spying on young ladies with a telescope from his attic.

Mr Maudley and his faithful feline friend soon settled in at the lighthouse. Maudley read book after book and wrote several more letters to his brother. In one of these letters, he wrote that he missed his old house and even his confounded gossiping neighbours. He also mentioned that he was having strange dreams about making love to young ladies. Maudley's brother wrote back, telling him that his unhealthy, lecherous dreams could be prevented if he would only say his prayers to the Almighty for an hour before retiring each night.

But Maudley began a diary, recording all his innermost and perverse thoughts about having sex with an imaginary young lady. His handwriting seemed to become more jagged and angular as he wrote about his carnal cravings and, at one point in the diary, he stabbed the page repeatedly with the point of his nib.

One sunny April morning, at 11 o'clock, Maudley's heart jumped when he glanced out from the window of his quarters in the lighthouse. On the rocks below strolled a pretty girl of about seventeen or eighteen. She wore a black straw boater and was holding up her skirt to her knees, as she carefully stepped around the deep pools on the rock. Under her arm was a long cane with a fine fishnet at the end and she carried a jar to hold any fish or crabs that she caught. The girl's name was Molly Jenkins and she had ventured on to Perch Rock at low tide, the only time the rock was accessible. In a few hours, the tide would turn and the rock would be covered again by twenty feet of seawater.

It is hard for a normal person to imagine the intense, erotic turmoil Maudley must have experienced when he first set eyes upon that young maiden on that sunny morning. What vile urges the lighthouseman felt that day will never be fully known but they must have driven him to violence, because Molly Jenkins disappeared that morning, although her black straw bonnet and fishing net were found that afternoon, drifting out with the tide.

The police asked Maudley if he had seen the missing girl and he said he had not. Yet in his secret diary, the old lighthouse keeper had sketched a girl wearing a boater with the words, "Molly, I am so sorry," scrawled next to it.

On 30 July of that year, at 9 o'clock at night, Jack Maudley's sixteen-year-old nephew, Richard, came to the lighthouse carrying a lantern across Perch Rock. The tide was starting to come in and the boy panicked and began to hammer on the main door of the lighthouse with his fist. His Uncle Jack opened the door a few minutes later and reluctantly admitted the boy into the building.

"I've run away from home, Uncle Jack," Richard told Maudley and followed him up the long winding steps to the living quarters.

"I told them I wanted to stay with you, Uncle, and my father said you ... er," the boy mumbled and could not finish the sentence.

"Your father said what?" Maudley retorted, as he halted on the steps and turned to face his nephew. His face looked sinister and distorted in the light of the lantern.

"Well, Uncle, father says you are ... a bit, erm a bit ... eccentric," Richard replied timidly and blushed deeply.

"What else did he say? Tell me!" shouted Maudley.

"He said you are always looking at ... at girls young enough to be your granddaughters," Richard continued.

"Hah! I couldn't give a damn what people say anymore," Maudley declared and continued to stomp up the stairs.

His black cat ran down to greet its master and arched its back as it spotted Richard and turned and fled up the flight of steps. Richard and his uncle sat in the living quarters playing chess for a couple of hours, then the boy said he would love to see the powerful light up in the turret of the lighthouse, so Maudley took him up to have a look. The view from the turret was a vast panorama of blackness. Now and then, the revolving beam of light made the foam of the waves below shimmer and sparkle, but otherwise a black void encompassed the building.

At midnight, a terrible thunderstorm rolled in from the Irish Sea. Gale force winds howled throughout the building and rain lashed at the windows of the turret. Lightning streaked down from the heavens and a searing, blinding bolt came down and struck the lightning conductor on the roof. Less than a heartbeat later, a powerful thunderclap shook the foundations of the lighthouse. Mr Maudley quickly escorted his nephew down to the living quarters for safety.

Richard sat in front of the small open fire in the room and listened to the storm raging outside. Then he heard the screams. At first, he thought it was the cat, but it soon became clear that it was a human wailing and screeching and it seemed to come from somewhere outside of the lighthouse.

"Uncle Jack?" Richard opened the door and crept up the steps leading to the turret. Up in the circular room of windows, was the trembling, jibbering wreck of Jack Maudley, on all fours. The black cat was purring and rubbing its affectionate face against his arm, thinking he was playing a game. All the time, the great dazzling light in the turret turned slowly on its axis, making Maudley's shadow waltz about the room.

"Uncle?"

Maudley jumped and turned to face him with a startled look. His face was white and his eyes bulged.

"Go back downstairs!" the keeper shouted and then looked back at the rain-battered windows.

"What's wrong, Uncle?" Richard asked.

Then he saw what was wrong. Something emerged from the stormy blackness. Something grotesque and hideous. It was the decomposed body of a girl. Her face was pale green and her eyes were empty black sockets. Black shiny seaweed hung from her skeletal, half-naked body. The ghoul's mouth opened wide and let out the terrible wailing sound that Richard had heard minutes before. She floated nearer and nearer to the windows of the turret, until the light swept over her rotting body.

Richard's stomach turned over and his knees felt weak. He became nauseous, yet he was transfixed by the grim sight. The ghoul looked like the mortal remains of a girl he had once had a crush on. It looked like the shell of Molly Jenkins.

Jack Maudley glanced up at the screaming vision and the terrible apparition pointed an accusing bony finger at him. The finger tapped repeatedly on the window. Then, as suddenly as it had started, the storm outside abated.

In the eerie calm, the corpse moaned, "You ... you killed me..."

In blind panic, Richard fled from the glass-lined turret and ran helter-skelter downstairs in the darkness until he reached the living quarters. He seized the lantern and raced down the winding steps.

A voice behind him screamed, "Richard, come back!"

"No!" Richard yelled. "You killed Molly! Father was right about you!"

The boy's heart pounded and he feared that his uncle would kill him too, now that he had discovered the horrible truth about Molly's mysterious disappearance.

When he reached the main door of the lighthouse, it was locked. Richard turned and saw his uncle's cat running silently down the steps out of the darkness. The cat arched its back and hissed aggressively at the boy, as it bared its pointed teeth.

Suddenly Jack Maudley loomed out of the darkness wielding a hatchet. His face had undergone a disturbing, bloodcurdling transformation and bore no resemblance to the jovial fellow who had been playing chess earlier.

"You shouldn't have come here tonight," snarled Maudley. "You should have stayed away from here. Look away," he demanded, ready to smash the teenager's skull to pieces as quickly as possible, to prevent unnecessary suffering.

"Please don't kill me, Uncle. I won't tell, I swear I won't tell," Richard pleaded.

"I know you won't tell, laddy. The dead can't speak," sneered Maudley, as he gritted his teeth and tapped his open hand with the blade of the hatchet, poised to strike.

Richard screamed, expecting to meet his doom, but then something darkly comical happened. The black cat got under Maudley's feet and the keeper fell down the last ten steps of the building. He tumbled down the steps, gashing his forehead on the final step. The evil old mariner lay there, motionless, as if dead. The hatchet fell from his hand and Richard noticed three keys tied with string to his uncle's belt. He pulled at them, but could not snap the strong yarn. So he removed the belt and slid the keys off. He tried the first key but it would not open the lock, nor would the second one; that was the key to Maudley's house. It had to be the third key. As Richard inserted it into the keyhole, a strong hand grabbed his ankle.

"Come here! You're not leaving here alive!" snarled Maudley.

He had regained consciousness. His cat purred with delight.

Richard let out another scream as his uncle reached for the hatchet. The lighthouse keeper seized its handle, but seemed too unsteady to stand up, instead attempting to hack his nephew to death from where he lay. He took an angry swipe at the boy's kneecap but Richard pulled his leg away just in time and the blade of the hatchet embedded itself deeply into the oaken door. As Maudley was trying to wrench the hatchet from the door, there was a pitiful moaning sound outside.

It was the ghoul – it was at the door.

Maudley was distracted by the spine-chilling sound and, at that tense moment, Richard managed to turn the key and pulled open the door. As he did so, the handle of the hatchet, stuck in the door, rammed into Maudley's eye, almost knocking him unconscious. Maudley let go of the boy's ankle and Richard ran screaming from the lighthouse and plunged into the sea. As he swam for the shore, choking with fear in the freezing saltwater, he managed to look back just once to see the ghoul entering the lighthouse. He could not be sure, but the terrified boy thought he heard a distant shrieking sound, as he thrashed about to save himself.

At first light, two detectives and five policemen arrived at Perch Rock at low tide. They found the main door of the lighthouse ajar and, on the steps, they came across the body of the keeper, Jack Maudley. There were marks on the walls where Maudley had struck out at someone with his hatchet but the police were at a loss to explain just who he had been fighting off. Stranger still, what could explain the strange rictus of death on the keeper's face? – the protruding tongue and bulging eyes which stared in terror? The detectives could see that someone had strangled the lighthouse keeper, someone with incredible strength but why had the killer left black, sinewy seaweed draped around Maudley's throat? There was one solitary clue at the murder scene. A small golden charm, in the form of an anchor, lay on the floor beside the throttled corpse. Detectives assumed it had probably belonged to the dead man but their enquiries failed to reach a satisfactory conclusion. Maudley's black cat was the only witness to the dramatic murder.

Richard Maudley told the detectives who had killed his insane uncle, but the law does not recognise the supernatural. Richard himself was suspected at first, but was subsequently cleared after a lengthy cross-examination. Through a strange quirk of fate, on the day of the terrible murder at the lighthouse, the badly decomposed body of Molly Jenkins was washed ashore on Perch Rock. The girl's mother and father came forward to identify her. Molly's father nodded in recognition but the dead girl's mother sobbed and said it could not be and the coroner asked her why not.

"She always wore her charm. A little gold anchor on a chain. I can't see any charm on this body."

The coroner shuddered when he heard this. He produced the little golden anchor found at the lighthouse and Molly's mother clutched it and broke down in tears.

The coroner was baffled. How did the charm end up at the lighthouse? If Maudley had killed the girl, who had strangled him? Even the warped diary of Maudley, which was later discovered at the lighthouse, with its incriminating reference to Molly, merely showed that the lighthouse keeper had an unbalanced mind – it didn't throw any light on the identity of the lighthouse strangler.

In the 1970s, New Brighton Lighthouse was sold off and refurbished. It was hired out to newly-married couples wanting somewhere unusual to spend their honeymoon. In 1973, one honeymooning couple allegedly heard an awful wailing sound, late one night, which seemed to come from the rock below. They never looked out of the windows, as they were too scared, but could it have been the tormented ghost of Molly Jenkins – the Lighthouse Ghoul?

DEATH WAS A STRANGER

O ne of the most curious stories I have looked into began one morning on a certain Liverpool street in the summer of 1997. A thin gangly man, aged about thirty, with long greasy hair, a faded blue tee shirt, stained jeans and grimy scuffed tennis shoes, made his way slowly down the street. His stubbled face was turned down to the pavement and he seemed to be so engrossed in his own thoughts that he was unaware of anything else around him. Tracking him at a walking pace, came a black BMW, cruising down the street a few yards behind him. In the car were three shaven-headed men, all in their twenties, and all wearing expensive, brand new track suits and immaculate, costly trainers. The windows were wound down and the skinheads surveyed the scruffily-dressed pedestrian with unpleasant smirks on their overly-tanned faces. The driver, in his designer shades, glanced back and forth between the street and the scruffy man.

Minutes later, the BMW rolled to a halt outside the large house where the three skinheads lived and worked. Their occupations lay in the criminal sphere. They committed burglaries on a regular basis and supplemented their income, whenever it was necessary, by distributing a variety of drugs to the neighbourhood junkies. However, in recent months, the trio had been forced to suspend their drug-pushing activities because a determined team of narcotics officers had been repeatedly raiding suspect premises in the area. We'll call the three shaven-headed n'er-do-wells Lee, Paul and Jason – not their real names.

The three of them sprang out of the BMW and jokingly seized the dishevelled man and jostled him towards the house. He meekly protested as two of the skinheads manhandled him down the hallway, through the back-kitchen, and out into the sunny back yard. The eldest of the criminals, Lee, went upstairs and returned shortly afterwards brandishing a pair of electric hair clippers, with no comb attachment fitted.

Jason and Paul roughly removed the stranger's clothes and when he pulled away and raised his voice in protest, they slapped his face and told him to shut up. Every item of clothing, including his dirty underwear, was removed from 'the hippy', as they now decided to call him, and Jason proceeded to shave off the poor man's hair with the clippers. The transformation from dishevelled, grubby, oily-haired beatnik into a streamlined hygienic skinhead was almost complete. The man was then bundled into an almost unbearably hot shower and scrubbed by six hands. Afterwards, he was shaved, and Hugo Boss cologne was slapped into his face, which was speckled with shaving cuts. As a finishing touch, the former drop-out was treated to some Calvin Klein underwear and a smart tracksuit from Wade Smith.

The newly groomed guest was disorientated and had severe doubts about the trio's motives and was anxious to leave the house, but Lee, Jason and Paul told him to relax and sat him at a table where one of them laid a thin line of coke.

"What's your name, mate?" Lee asked, putting his arm around the unknown man.

"John," came the reply.

"Well, John, have some whiz."

Lee pushed John's face down towards the line of white powder.

"No, I'm sorry, but I'm not into drugs," John mumbled, apologetically.

"Are you a retard?" Jason asked, seriously. He thought John's apparent slowness of mind and clumsy actions belied some kind of mental problem.

Lee's temper flared. He was a very muscular man and he grabbed John's arm and yanked it up his back, then pushed his face into the coke powder. John groaned – then breathed out heavily blowing away the powder, which quickly resulted in him receiving a beating from all three. He was bundled into a spare room in the house and kept there under lock and key. John tried to shout for help but his captors would blast music as loud as they could from a CD player to blot out the noise. In any case, the neighbours were so afraid of the drug dealers, that they never complained either to them, or the police.

Three days later, John was still being held captive at the house, when he was escorted downstairs to a back room where Lee, Paul and Jason were smoking marijuana. It was eleven o'clock in the evening and the vertical blinds were open, admitting silver stripes of moonlight from a full summer moon into the room. A radio was whispering on low volume, and a crimson lava lamp undulated hypnotically on the mantelpiece.

John was pushed into a deep leather armchair, while Lee sprawled out on a sofa, and talked about feeling tranquil, and Paul and Jason sat on the floor, gazing up at a tank of tropical fish on the sideboard. John refused to smoke any pot, but Lee was so drugged, that this time he took no offence and accepted his captive's refusal. As the night wore on, the skinheads lost all sense of time, and the drug seemed to remove the false personas of the street-hard tough-guys.

"Wonder if a swan can break your arm, just by flapping its wing," Lee suddenly mused, and started to giggle, thinking about the way his father would warn him not to go near the swans on Sefton Park's boating lake when he was a boy.

"Wonder why the moon's round and not square," Paul idly remarked, watching the moon sinking ever so slowly beyond the silhouetted rooftops.

Jason exhaled a perfect smoke ring from his rolled-up joint and murmured, "Round is natural."

All the external doors were locked, and so John was allowed to make himself a cup of tea in the kitchen. The effects of the drug and the mellowness of the summer evening were conducive to an unexpected mystical discussion about life after death among the criminals.

"I reckon there's something after this, deffo," Jason said, staring at the luminescent graphic equaliser display on the radio.

"Yeah, a six foot hole," was Lee's response.

"Yeah, but say you get cremated?" Paul asked.

"Okay, then, there's just an urnful of ashes. A mixture of other people's ashes mixed in as well probably."

"What d'you mean?" Jason asked.

"I heard that they save a few bob by cremating a few bodies at once," Lee told him with a smirk.

"That's well out of order," Jason protested.

The subject turned to ghost stories, and each of the skinheads told a supernatural tale, then they asked John if he knew any ghost stories.

John shook his head, "No, but a lot of strange things have happened to me though."

"What like?" Lee said, suddenly propping himself up on one arm and taking an interest. He rested on his stomach, then focused his attention on the abducted 'guest'.

"People around me always die," said John, flatly.

At that moment, Lee, Paul and Jason felt a sudden cold current of air from the open window brush against the back of their necks.

"How d'you mean, 'always die'?" asked Lee.

"I've lost my entire family to accidents, cancer, suicides. I've had five girlfriends in my life and they've all died within months of my meeting them. I'm like the angel of death. Like a fatal jinx on everybody I meet."

"Maybe you're just unlucky," Jason said, after a long tense pause.

"No, it's more than that," John replied, "I'm like the Grim Reaper, and I don't know why. When I was young I was put in one school after another. Teachers died: in fires, car crashes … Friends I made choked on sweets, were murdered, or knocked down … The schools would change, but the outcome was always the same. It's gone on and on and I'm so tired of it. Behind me there's a trail of dead bodies."

"No way!" Lee said, and, he saw how nervous Jason and Paul seemed all of a sudden.

That night, when John was put back in his room, the skinheads argued amongst themselves.

"I'll let him go in a few days. I'm just hanging on to him for a laugh," Lee explained to his younger accomplices.

"There's something not right about him, Lee," Jason said. "He gives me the creeps."

"Just let him go now," Paul suggested. "What's the point of keeping him?"

"You big soft tart," said Lee. "In a few days we'll let him go. He's just a weirdo. Now get to bed."

On the following morning, Jason was soaping himself in the shower, when he felt a hard, round lump under his armpit. It was not at all painful, but it was very definitely a lump, and he panicked.

He told his mates about it as they ate their cornflakes, trying not to sound as if he was scared. Paul advised him to go to the doctor's straight away, but Lee dismissed the lump, saying it was probably just an overactive sweat gland.

Later that day, there was a frantic knocking at the door. It was Lee's mother, and she was in floods of tears. Her brother – Lee's Uncle David – had just died. Lee's dad had died when he was a child and his Uncle David had raised him like a father. Lee's mother said she had found her brother hanging out of his bed, clutching his chest and gasping for breath. He had asked her to get an ambulance, but he died from what looked like a heart attack before she could even get to the telephone.

During the confusion, as Lee rushed to his mother's home, John slipped out of the house, back into the obscurity of the street.

Within a week, Paul was dead from an accidental heroin overdose. His blue bloated body had lain decomposing in the shared house while Lee stayed a week with his grief-stricken mother. When he found Paul's corpse, it was crawling with maggots and bluebottles.

Jason did go to the doctors with his lump and was quickly diagnosed with cancer. He was sent to Clatterbridge Hospital to undergo a programme of intense chemotherapy.

A month later, Lee's mother was deserted by her lover of six years, and that, coupled with the traumatic loss of her brother, caused her to suffer a nervous breakdown which resulted in her needing treatment in a psychiatric hospital.

From Clatterbridge, Jason wrote to me about these tragic incidents, and the claims of the mysterious John. He was convinced that John was some kind of harbinger of death and some months after writing the letter, he lost his battle against cancer.

In 1999, Lee committed suicide by attaching a pipe to his car exhaust and feeding it into his BMW in a garage at a house in Brighton. At the time of his death, there were rumours that he had recently been diagnosed with AIDs.

Was the spate of deaths nothing more than a cluster of dark coincidences? Or did the weird stranger actually cast a shadow of death on his captors?

MURDER FORESEEN

In May 1950, a thirty-two-year-old Tuebrook woman, Mary Jones, started work at the Littlewoods Pools firm on Edge Lane, near the Botanic Park. Mary was separated from her husband, and considered herself to be single. Her five-year-old son Bobby was staying with his grandmother for the time being.

One night she went to a pub with a few friends, and she met a very handsome man of about forty. He was rather shabbily dressed, but Mary had never seen anyone so attractive. He had curly black hair and unusual, sky-blue eyes. He was also quite stocky. He smiled a few times at Mary, then came over and asked her if he could buy her a drink. Mary accepted, and as the night wore on, the two of them left the others and went to have a drink in a corner of the pub.

The man's name was Ted Lawless and at first he was very reluctant to say just exactly what he did for a living, but then he changed his mind and decided to tell Mary. He said he was a scrap metal merchant. Mary did not really care what Ted did, because she already thought there was something very charismatic about him. Ted lived near Fontenoy Gardens, where he owned and ran a small scrapyard, but he happened to be in Tuebrook on this particular night, to buy some old lead pipes from the pub landlord.

When the pub closed, Ted kissed Mary and arranged to see her again at the Locarno ballroom the following week. She was very excited about the date and when it finally came, they danced the night away. Mary still had not told Ted that she had a husband, and this guilty secret kept nagging away at her; she should have told him when they first met. When they left the Locarno, Ted convinced Mary to go home with him and she stayed the night.

The following morning he was unable to hide his feelings and asked her to live with him, but she made excuses, saying she had to look after her mother, who was not too well at the moment.

Ted Lawless held Mary's face close to his.

"Look, I'm of Romany descent. My grandmother was part gypsy, and I can just look into your eyes and know you're not telling me the truth," he said.

"What are you talking about?" asked Mary, averting her eyes and feeling distinctly uncomfortable.

Ted grabbed her hand and examined her palm. He frowned and announced that she was married and had a son. Mary thought he must have learnt this information from one of her friends.

"Who told you, huh? Was it Maureen?" she demanded, presuming it was her friend at Littlewoods who had spilled the beans.

Ted shook his head and explained that he could read information from Mary herself. He reached out and hugged her, declaring passionately, "It doesn't matter, Mary. I can't let you go."

A week later, something unusual happened. Mary visited the scrapyard near Fontenoy Gardens and found it deserted. The gates were chained up. A man across the street told Mary that Mr Lawless had moved away and that the yard had closed down. Someone said that had moved to Preston.

Mary was frantic, and heartbroken – just when she thought she had found true happiness, it had been snatched away. A few days later, a letter arrived at Littlewoods Pools, addressed to Mary Jones. The letter was from Ted and in it, he explained that he had been forced to leave Mary after experiencing three terrifying nightmares. He had dreamt that he had strangled her after he had found her in the embrace of another man. In the dream he had knifed the man, and then strangled her to death in a fit of jealous rage. The same realistic dream had recurred on the following night. Ted explained that he had had such dreams before, and they had always come true, so he regarded them as forebodings, not to be ignored. In the third dream, he had been reading a copy of the *Liverpool Echo*, and the double murder he had committed had made front page news. The dream had been so real that Lawless was even able to read the print in the article, and he saw that the name of the man he had knifed had been Patrick Berry, aged thirty-three, from Fairfield. Finally, Lawless had seen a noose dangling down before his eyes and he had woken up in a cold sweat.

Mary assumed that Ted had made up this strange story as an excuse to leave her, as she knew no one by the name of Patrick Berry. But five months later, a new barman started work at the pub which Mary frequented with her friends. The man's name was Pat, and it transpired that he was from Fairfield. After a short while he started to court Mary Jones. Naturally, Mary recoiled in shock when she learnt that his surname was Berry. Without explaining her motives she immediately stopped seeing him there and then.

MADAME LaLAURIE

Marie McCarthy arrived at Liverpool in the summer of 1839 on a merchant ship called the *St Lawrence*, which had sailed from New York. Among the crew of that ship was a certain eighteen-year-old cabin boy named Herman Melville. The teenager was destined to become one of the greatest writers of all time one day, whilst Marie McCarthy was destined for a grisly date with her conscience.

Beneath her hood, Marie's long dark hair was tied up in a knot, high upon her head, with well sculpted curls and loops above the ears. Through the rain of an out-of-season downpour, her beautiful but cold blue eyes surveyed the dock, and the stevedores, and the crowds of people at the quayside, surging forward to greet family, friends and loved ones newly arrived from New York. She had no loved one waiting for her in this foreign land, only a business acquaintance of her late husband's; a man named Troy Ellis, and she was to meet him in the Liver Hotel at Waterloo.

Later that day, a carriage took Marie to the hotel, and there she met Mr Ellis. He, like Marie, was from Louisiana, and spoke with a southern drawl that the young Creole lady found comforting being so far from her home. Miss McCarthy rested for three days at the Liver Hotel, while Mr Ellis made arrangements to provide her with the type of luxurious accommodation to which she had been accustomed in New Orleans, before she was forced to take flight. A house on Abercromby Square, close to St Catherine's Church, was bought outright. Miss McCarthy had more than enough money to buy fifty such houses, although no one was certain of the source of such flowing finance. She rarely attended balls and soirées, but when she did Marie McCarthy gave away little information about her past and the origin of her wealth. Gold diggers tried to woo her and bank managers tried to advise her, but it was always in vain. Mr Ellis played a protective role and would try to intervene and fend off any unwelcome attention.

Strange rumours began to circulate about the house on Abercromby Square concerning dreadful female screams heard in the dead of night. Some thought the wealthy young American was demented with having so much money, yet no love in her life.

In 1841, a twenty-year-old footman named William Priest was employed at the house of mystery, and the tall athletic youth soon became romantically involved with Miss McCarthy, despite the efforts of Mr Ellis to thwart what he considered to be a highly unsuitable romance. William and Marie went on a romantic sojourn to Paris, but whilst in the French capital, Marie encountered two gentlemen who called her 'Madame LaLaurie', and spat at her and accused her of being evil. Miss McCarthy and her lover were forced to flee in a carriage to avoid a scene, and Marie assured William that it had all been a case of mistaken identity.

Back in Liverpool, strange things began to happen at the house on Abercromby Square. The sounds of chains being rattled were heard to come up the stairs at midnight, and in the early hours of the morning, the sound of women and children wailing could be heard. One evening at eleven o'clock, William Priest was lying besides Marie McCarthy in her four poster bed, when they heard the distressing sound of chains rattling nearby. On this occasion, a procession of silhouettes crossed the wall at the end of the room. The shadows of men, women and children with chains leading from one neck to the other, walked in a single file across the lavishly decorated walls. Upon seeing this uncanny spectacle, Marie let out a scream and hid beneath the covers.

The hauntings seemed to follow Marie, whether she was in her bedroom or at a hotel, and by the Christmas of 1841, she suffered a mental breakdown. When William Priest called at the house on New Year's Eve, he was told that Marie had taken her own life by slitting her wrists, three days before. Troy Ellis showed him the blood-soaked bed, and the open coffin. William wept over the coffin, then left the house for good, unaware of the true identity of the woman he loved.

For many years in Liverpool, nobody knew the dark history of Marie McCarthy, and in 1841, the inquisitive people of Liverpool's élite society would have paid dearly to learn what I am about to relate to you.

Marie McCarthy was, in fact, Delphine McCarty LaLaurie, a wealthy socialite from New Orleans. In 1831, she and her husband, the eminent physician, Louis LaLaurie, purchased a beautiful, majestic-looking mansion at 1140 Royal Street. Madame LaLaurie revelled in throwing lavish soirées in which she entertained the most prominent people in New Orleans with no expense spared. Madame LaLaurie was not only renowned for her spectacular parties though; she was perhaps better known for her immense retinue of well-behaved slaves. At this time, there were rumours about Delphine's cruelty towards her slaves, but no one could have guessed the full shocking extent of her barbarity.

Delphine was a woman of striking, angelic beauty, and when she travelled through New Orleans in her sleek phaeton coach, driven by a regally dressed slave, she was quite a sight to behold. On many occasions, Madame LaLaurie would throw a handful of pennies on to the cobblestones for the children. To the young ladies of New Orleans, Delphine McCarty LaLaurie was a role model, but behind the splendour and respectability, there lurked a monster of a woman.

In the kitchens of the LaLaurie mansion, Delphine kept the black cook chained within twenty feet of the fireplace, where her indulgent and sumptuous meals were prepared. No visitors were ever aware of this shocking state of affairs, because people from outside the mansion were never allowed into the kitchens.

One afternoon in 1833, a neighbour of the LaLauries heard a child's scream at their courtyard. The neighbour peeped out through the lace curtains and saw a little black slave girl of about eight years of age, running across the courtyard of the LaLaurie mansion, and in hot pursuit was Delphine LaLaurie, brandishing a bullwhip and screaming at the child in French. The slave girl, Leah, had been combing her mistress's long tresses, and had caught a knot in Delphine's hair, which was pulled by the comb. In a fit of rage, Madame LaLaurie had seized a bullwhip and chased the petrified little girl out of her boudoir.

The neighbour watched in horror as Delphine chased the girl up four storeys and on to a balcony that ran over the carriageway. As Madame LaLaurie ascended the stairs with the whip, Leah tried to climb over the rail of the balcony, but lost her footing and plunged back down to the courtyard. Her limp and broken body lay there, totally lifeless, as Madame LaLaurie's cousin arrived just metres away in his carriage. He was astonished to witness the tragedy. The neighbour continued to observe the dreadful proceedings, and she watched Delphine LaLaurie pick up Leah's tiny body and take it into the house. The same neighbour also observed shadowy figures burying the slave girl's body in the corner of the courtyard after dark.

The authorities investigated the concerned neighbour's allegations, and in the end Madame LaLaurie was merely fined three hundred dollars for not declaring the death.

At that time in New Orleans, there was a slave-protection law in force which ordained that slaves who were subjected to cruelty would be automatically taken from their owner and sold at public auction. However, slaves that were taken from Madame LaLaurie and sold at auction often ended up as her property again, because the sadistic socialite would arrange for her rich relatives to buy the slaves at the auctions and then give them back to her.

The misery and cruelty which the slaves endured at the hands of the deceptively angel-faced woman continued for some time, until April 1834, when the cook announced to the other slaves that it would be better to die than to live such a wretched life at the LaLaurie mansion, and she set the house on fire. The fire brought the immediate attention of both the local populace and the fire brigade. When the firemen turned up at the mansion, they were directed by the slaves to a small attic crawlspace that was bolted and locked from the outside. Whimpers and moans were heard from inside this confined, claustrophobic room, and a battering ram was used to gain access. The firemen had been exposed to death and disfigurement many times before, yet even the seasoned fire officers were not prepared for the hideous sights which awaited them within the tiny room.

Inside were at least a dozen slaves, chained to the walls. They were maimed and disfigured, their bones protruding through their skin from chronic malnutrition. It was subsequently discovered that many of these poor souls had been the subject of crude medical experiments. One man had been turned into a eunuch by barbaric surgery. The most horrifying sight was that of a woman locked inside a cage small enough to accommodate only a small dog. Her arms had been amputated at the hand of Madame LaLaurie and her skin appeared to have been peeled off in sections. Another victim of the inhumane Delphine LaLaurie had all of her arms and legs broken and the joints reset at odd angles so that she could only move along on her stomach in a hideous crablike manner.

One wild-eyed woman, once freed from her shackles, ran in terror past the firemen and jumped through a window immediately to her death. Two of the slaves had died from smoke inhalation, but the ones that survived were given sympathetic pensions. The slaves revealed how Madame LaLaurie whipped them mercilessly each morning after breakfast to satisfy her sadistic cravings. As firemen sifted through the fire-damaged mansion, they came across a variety of body parts from the mutilated slaves, stored in jars and upon shelves.

As the disgusting news about Madame LaLaurie's treatment of her slaves spread, the enraged townspeople demanded rough justice and sought her out, but Delphine and Louis LaLaurie, and their loyal coachman, had already fled from

New Orleans. The LaLauries abandoned the coachman once they were safe, and he made the mistake of returning to New Orleans, where the mob stabbed the horses and destroyed the carriage. The coachman was battered to within an inch of his life, but was lucky enough to live through the ordeal. The appalled crowds then returned to the LaLaurie mansion and burnt what remained of the former grand residence to the ground.

It was said that Louis LaLaurie died in mysterious circumstances not long afterwards, but no trace of Madame LaLaurie could be found, although there were many rumours about her whereabouts. Some said she had gone into hiding in France, whereas others claimed that the evil woman had been seen in New York, waiting for a passage to England.

In fact, Madame LaLaurie had boarded the *St Lawrence* at New York under the assumed name of Marie McCarthy, and with a trunk full of diamonds, gold and jewellery, she had headed for a port in England that had always had amicable connections with the American South – Liverpool. It seems though, that the vengeful spectres of her victims had also travelled with the wicked, butchering murderess, and had haunted her conscience until she was forced to take her own life.

Some say that the body of Delphine LaLaurie was shipped back to New Orleans to be buried by relatives at a secret location. We may never know where her body lies, but I think we can safely assume where her soul is.

LODGE LANE VAMPIRE

HAUNTED LIVERPOOL 2

There have been sporadic reports of vampires on the loose in Liverpool. In February 1983, a young single mother, living in a bedsit in Lodge Lane with her eight-month-old baby, had the constant feeling that she was being watched. She was not the superstitious or paranoid type, but from the day that she moved into the bedsit, she had experienced the horrible sensation of being observed by someone or something next door, especially at night.

In the end, the edgy electric atmosphere in the bedsit became so intense, that the woman went to Wavertree Road Police Station and complained to the rather bemused constable about the unpleasant feeling of being watched in the spooky flat. The policeman shook his head and said that he was sorry, but there was nothing he could do. It wasn't a police matter. The girl began to sob hysterically and she begged him to send an officer round to investigate the flat adjacent to her bedsit because she felt as if the place was radiating evil. To placate her and get her off the premises, he promised to send someone around to look into the matter.

That night, at 10pm, the young woman was watching the *News At Ten*, trying to take her mind off her predicament, when a series of loud thumps from next door nearly made her jump out of her skin. She looked nervously out of the window and saw, to her relief, that there was a police car parked down below in the street. The police must have responded to her plea and were inspecting the next door flat – hence the banging noises. She put her ear to the wall and could hear the strains of a policeman's radio blurting out.

Later that night the police called at her flat and revealed to her what they had discovered in the flat next door. Apparently, the previous occupier had painted all of the walls and ceilings black and dotted them with mysterious pentagrams and other occult symbols. In the middle of the floor there was a large, mud-covered coffin, whose wooden sides had begun to crumble with age. It must have been at least a hundred years old. It had probably been robbed from a tomb in a local graveyard, but it was now empty and there were no traces of the corpse it had once contained. The nameplate was too rusted to be decipherable. Next to the coffin was a mysterious book entitled *The Book of Shadows*. Most disturbing of all, next to the book was a milk bottle – which was found to contain a small amount of clotted human blood.

The police made enquiries in the neighbourhood, but no one in the street could remember who the occupier of that flat was and he, or she, never returned, but even the hard-boiled, streetwise policemen claimed that they had experienced an icy chill as they entered the flat. As for the young mother, she was not prepared to stay and see if the mysterious occupant would return or not and she left that night with her baby and went to stay with her auntie on the Wirral.

MESSAGE FROM THE GLASS

In the 1970s, a group of seven Liverpool University students lodged together at a house on Liverpool's Edge Lane. One evening, one of the students was mooching about up in the attic, when he found an old Edwardian ouija board, and it wasn't long before he and his friends were experimenting with the upturned glass on the board. Their seven index fingers rested on the inverted wine-glass, and, unlike most people who dabble with the ouija board for amusement, the students took what they were doing very seriously. The time was eleven o'clock at night, and a single candle lit the room.

After a few moments, the glass started to move steadily, and the students noted that it was sliding towards the letter 'C'. Then it moved to the letter 'H'. Within thirty seconds the name 'Charlie' had been spelled out. One of the students looked uneasily around the darkened room, and in a sombre voice said, "Hello Charlie". The glass seemed to jolt, as if the force moving it was excited. One of the students, a young man who was rather frightened by the proceedings, got up and walked over to the light switch. He clicked the switch – but the light wouldn't come on. He clicked it again and again, but the light bulb still refused to shine, so the youth had no choice but to rejoin his friends, feeling rather uneasy. There was just one finger remaining on the glass, and as it slid about the board, the other students noted the garbled message it spelt out. It was a person's name, followed by the two words, 'murdered me'. Then came three more words, 'I was hanged'. The students assumed that they were conversing with a spirit from the age of capital punishment, which they knew had ended in the 1960s.

Moments later, another spirit came through, and this spirit was very mischievous, because it initially claimed that it was the deceased uncle of one of the female students, and it even seemed to know all the details about her uncle's life. However, the presence started spelling out obscene words and even claimed the girl would 'die nasty' when she was thirty. The students ended up fleeing from the flat, and as they did so, a shadowy hand appeared in mid-air and pinched the candle's wick, plunging the room into darkness. When they later returned to the room with torches, they found the impressions of tooth-marks in the candle.

111

When the landlord heard about the ouija's information regarding the spirit, Charlie, and the message about being hanged, he cast his mind back to a mysterious murder that had taken place just a few doors away, at Number 62 Edge Lane, in 1946.

At around ten o'clock on the Saturday night of 2 February 1946, fourteen-year-old Ernest Johnson from Number 13 Watford Road, in Anfield, decided to call upon his cousin Charles Greeney, the eleven-year-old son of Mrs Greeney, a money-lender, and Charles, a plasterer. When Ernest Johnson arrived at Number 62, he found that the front door was open, and all the lights were on in the large, eleven-room house. The place had been ransacked and it was obvious that there had been a break-in.

When Ernest looked in the kitchenette, he found the schoolboy, Charlie Greeney, hanging by his neck from the clothes rack, and he seemed to be dead. Ernest ran out of the house and informed the neighbours next door about the murder. He then rushed just two-hundred yards to a hotel where the dead boy's parents were having their usual Saturday evening drink. The parents returned to the house and the father took Charlie down from the rack and tried to give him a drink to resuscitate him, but it was no use. He was dead.

The property that had been taken from the house was valued at six hundred pounds. Expensive clocks, a huge fawn Wilton carpet, brand new suits, fur coats and various other expensive items had been stolen, but the safe in the office where Mrs Greeney carried out her money-lending business was untouched. The family's seven-month-old bull terrier pup was in the yard outside the kitchen where the hanging had taken place, and although the pup barked whenever strangers called, the neighbours said he had not made a sound that night. The only clue to the burglary and murder was a plain Albion van that had been seen parked on Dorothy Street, just around the corner from the house. Chief Superintendent Fothergill wondered if the burglars had been recognised by Charlie, and they had killed him to ensure he remained silent. Or, as another detective suggested, had the burglars broken into the house and found the boy hanging as they were ransacking the place?

Five men were soon arrested for the burglary and four of them were also held on suspicion of murder. A sixth man was arrested in Gibraltar. All four swore they had not killed Charlie Greeney. Two of the men said that when they broke into the house, they saw Charlie apparently standing on a chair in front of a fireplace with his back towards them. He was not moving, and they at first assumed he was deaf, so they proceeded to burgle the other rooms. The inquest proved that Charlie could not possibly have hanged himself and hoisted his own body up on to the clothes rack, but the investigation eventually ground to a frustrating halt.

The four accused men were found not guilty of murder and the judge summed up the strange case by saying, "Although we are not certain that it was an accident, we are not certain that it was not." The hanging of Charles Greeney is therefore still an unsolved mystery.

The seven students who communicated with the spirit of Charlie – who said he had died by being hanged – were from Wiltshire, Leeds and Hull, and they knew nothing of the Greeney murder case of 1946. Was it all coincidence and hysteria, or did the spirit of the deceased schoolboy try to contact the living to identify his murderer?

Whispers from a Death Mask

Haunted Liverpool 1

In January 1922, a twenty-four-year-old auburn-haired woman, Maggie, came out of the Vines public house, which still stands on the corner of Lime Street and Copperas Hill. She had arranged to meet a young man called Rex, who worked in a nearby hotel but there was no sign of him. Maggie was shivering in the icy wind that blew down Lime Street, when a voice behind her asked, "Looking for someone, Miss?"

Maggie spun round and saw a small man, about five feet three inches in height, standing there with a childish smile on his face. The man looked shabby and had stubble on his chin.

"Yes, my boyfriend. He said he'd be here at eight o'clock," Maggie replied, glancing up and down the street once more.

"What's your boyfriend like?"

"He's got blond hair and he's quite tall."

"There's a fellow of that description talking to a man around the corner."

"Really?" said Maggie and looked up Copperas Hill.

"I'll show you where he is," said the man and took Maggie by the wrist along the street towards a narrow lane that used to stand near Bolton Street. As he reached the dimly-lit lane, he produced a small clasp knife and held it against Maggie's delicate neck.

"Don't scream, or I'll cut your throat!" he threatened.

He then pushed her into an alleyway and committed a serious sexual assault, throughout which he ground his teeth loudly. Finally, he punched Maggie in the face and she landed on a stack of wooden crates at the back of the pub.

After the attack, the police stepped up patrols in the area but, for a fortnight, there were no further attacks. Then, on the night of 24 January, a small, middle-aged man seized a prostitute in Lord Nelson Street and, after an unsuccessful rape attempt, stole her earrings and purse before running off, laughing in a high-pitched voice as he went. Again, the police were unable to catch him. Three days later, there were two more attacks on women in Liverpool, one in Cropper Street, where a policeman gave chase to the rapist before he could assault his victim and the other, a mere forty-five minutes later, in the very alley off Copperas Hill where he had first struck. During this assault, the man again ground his teeth and then bit the twenty-one-year-old victim's shoulder. He then ripped off her gold chain and locket and escaped into the night.

The police had no inkling as to who the offender was, until an old lady walked into Cheapside Bridewell and said that she had seen a small man with evil, shifty-looking eyes on many occasions hanging around Copperas Hill and she was sure that he was the rapist. She told officers how he stared at young women's legs walking up Lime Street. The police sent out plain clothes detectives to patrol the street and, within hours, the little man appeared, ogling at every woman who passed him. The detectives followed him as he walked down Lime Street, stopped and took out a bunch of keys to unlock the door of one of Liverpool's famous attractions, Reynold's Waxworks.

The police grabbed the man, one Alfie Begg, a fifty-seven-year-old bachelor, who lived with his mother and worked as a temporary watchman at the wax museum. As the detectives took Begg into the waxworks, in handcuffs, he started to cry, "I'm innocent of these crimes. It's all Deeming's doing."

"Deeming? Who's he?" one of the detectives asked.

It was decidedly eerie down in the Chamber of Horrors. There was a clockwork-driven model of Marie Antoinette being guillotined and graphic torture scenes in a realistic mock-up of the Inquisition. What was even more gruesome, was the line of life-like heads of famous murderers from the 1840s to the present day. All the heads were actual plaster cast impressions, taken from the heads of the killers after they had been hanged. One of the heads was the death mask of one of the most notorious mass-murderers of all time, Frederick Deeming, the Birkenhead-born psychopath who had killed every member of his own family and then danced on their graves with his next victim.

Mr Begg pointed his handcuffed hands at the head of the killer and announced, "Meet Mr Deeming."

The detectives looked at each other and shook their heads. The nightwatchman was obviously mentally disturbed.

Begg then addressed the death mask, "Say hello to our visitors."

"He's not saying anything till he sees his solicitor, eh?" smirked one of the detectives.

Then a squeaky trembling voice said, "I hate coppers."

The detectives were naturally startled by the sound and looked about the other gruesome wax effigies, expecting to see someone hiding in the darkness, but there was no one else about.

"You'd better come with us, Mr Begg," said a policeman, feeling a bit edgy.

He secretly hoped that Begg had a talent for ventriloquism.

"If I promise not to hurt any women again, will you leave me alone?" Mr Begg asked, childishly.

"Come along, sir," said one of the detectives, escorting him away from the rogue's gallery.

Begg started to cry and turned back to the death-mask of Frederick Deeming saying, "They're taking me away and it's all your fault, Mr Deeming! You made me do it!"

At the bridewell, Begg repeated that he was just a simple man who had been driven to crime because the murderer, Deeming, had forced him into carrying out the rapes and robberies. The clasp knife Begg had used was not his, but had been taken from one of the waxwork exhibits. Several people who had known Alfie Begg said the man was a stable, but somewhat slow person, not known for the quickness of his mind. He had no criminal record and his one claim to fame was that he had once rescued a dog from a frozen lake in Sefton Park. When a psychiatrist questioned him about his conversations with the sinister talking head, Alfie Begg replied, "Mr Deeming's spirit said it was really scared because the Devil had found out that he had been hiding in his death mask for years."

"What will the Devil do to poor Mr Deeming's spirit, now that he's found him?" chuckled the psychiatrist.

Alfie Begg looked worried.

"Mr Deeming said that Satan would claw his spirit back to Hell. I saw Satan once. He came up, out of the ground, in the Chamber of Horrors. I was scared."

"What did the Devil look like, Alfie?" asked the psychiatrist.

"Bloody horrible. I had nightmares. Satan is like a tall, dark-haired man but he was surrounded by flames. All these terrible screaming voices were all around him. He said they were the damned – bad people trapped in Hell."

The psychiatrist scribbled Alfie's words down, dismissing him as a schizophrenic. Then Alfie held out his left hand and pointed to his wrist. There was a thick straight scar across it.

"The Devil touched me there and burned me. I cried and he just laughed. He said he'd be back one day for Deeming and that he'd burn the place down."

Later that week, the police psychiatrist heard that Reynold's Wax Museum

116

had been gutted by a fire of unknown origin. The psychiatrist visited the burnt-out ruin of the waxworks and a fire officer took him down the steps to what remained of the Chamber of Horrors. In the grotesque mass of melted figures was one exhibit that had almost survived the previous night's mysterious inferno – the distorted head of Frederick Deeming. The heat had partially melted the head and its jaws had buckled open, making Deeming appear to cry out in agony. The psychiatrist and the fire officer were leaving the shel of the building when a faint voice cried out, "Help me, Jesus!" They turned around but there was no one about.

Stranger still, when the psychiatrist visited Alfie Begg in a mental institution later that week and told him about the fire and Deeming's partially melted death mask, Begg replied, "I know! Mr Deeming told me. He was here last night, you see, then the Devil dragged him off to Hell."

The Man in Black

One evening in 1932, on the night of a full moon, nine people arrived at a house in St John's Road in Waterloo. Some of the nosier neighbours, twitching their net curtains, wondered what the nature of the gathering was. Was some party imminent perhaps? Was it somebody's birthday? Had they known the truth, they would have been scandalised, for the people were actually assembling for a séance. It is an ancient belief that the number of people attending a séance should be divisible by three, and so these nine people from Waterloo, Crosby and Litherland seated themselves around a large round table in an upstairs room, ready for what some of them regarded as a bit of fun, and others as an adventure into the unknown.

In the centre of the table was a loaf of bread. Bread placed in the middle of the table in such a way is also part of an age-old custom, and is thought to attract the spirits for some obscure reason. Three candles were lit around the bread, and the heavy velvet curtains were drawn and overlapped so that not even a single ray of moonlight could enter the room. The men and women each spread their hands out on the table so that they touched one another by the tips of their little fingers. The participants then intoned these words together:

"Spirit, we bring you gifts from life into death. Commune with us, spirit, and move among us."

Everyone present waited eagerly for a response.

Two raps from the spirit were expected, and the sitters waited in tense silence. This was the first time a séance had been held at this particular address on St John's Road. Other séances held by the group at other addresses had all been huge anti-climaxes. Little did anyone know that this address held a terrible dark secret. This was one house where supernatural dabblings of any kind should definitely not have been carried out.

The sound of a clock striking midnight could be heard in the living room downstairs. The candles started to flicker on the table, and as the midnight chimes started to fade, everyone present felt something vibrating through the table. The floor and the entire room began to shake. Then, suddenly, the curtains flew fully open as if pulled apart by invisible hands – to reveal a sinister figure in a long black cape standing there. The strange outdated figure was seen as a silhouette because of the full moon shining down behind it through the window. It flitted forward towards the startled people at the table, and it placed its hand on the shoulder of the man acting as the medium of the table. This man shuddered because, even through his clothes, he could feel that the hand of the supernatural stranger was colder than ice. Everybody then gasped in fear and amazement as the figure vanished instantly with a loud flutter of its cape.

The gas lamps on the wall were quickly lit, and everybody wondered what the significance of the sinister vision was, and why it had touched the medium's shoulder. Everybody agreed that the man in the black cloak had given off a strong aura of evil which had permeated the whole room.

On the following morning, the medium from that séance – who lived in Crosby – was found dead in his bed, and on his pallid face, was a look of the utmost horror.

The case then deepened when other members of the séance discovered from various people in St John's Road that the place where they had held the séance had quite a reputation for being haunted. The man in black with the long cloak had put in an appearance at least forty years before, and he was reputed to be a harbinger of death.

Now, I was intrigued to receive a letter in early 2003 from a Mrs Stephenson who once lived at the haunted house in Waterloo, but who now lives in Australia. She said that, in 1976, a female relative was returning home one night, just after nine o'clock, and as she entered the house, which was in total darkness, she noticed a faint glow at the top of the stairs, and silhouetted against this glow was the figure of a man in a cape. The woman froze in fear, and cried out, "Who's that?" When there was no reply, she realised that she was seeing the spectre she had often heard her mother talk about. It was supposed to appear when one of the family was about to come to harm. On previous occasions it had put in an appearance before the death of her grandmother, and on another occasion it had materialised days before her brother had suffered a heart attack.

The woman panicked because she was convinced that the phantom was going to attack her. It definitely gave out a strong impression of menace. When the woman switched the light on, the figure instantly disappeared.

Nine days later, the woman's brother was seriously injured in a car crash, but fortunately recovered. The figure was about five feet ten inches in height, had short black hair, and wore a cloak that covered its legs.

In 1987, Mrs Stephenson emigrated to Australia with her family and young daughter. Then, a few years ago, she returned to Waterloo, and during the visit, she and her brother and daughter went to visit the old house on St John's Road to reminisce, and during the visit her daughter disappeared. She had wandered off by herself into a room upstairs. This girl had never been told about the incidents with the man in black. When her mother caught up with her, she was shaking from head to foot. Something had obviously terrified her. She told her mother that a man's voice had urged her to pick up a shard of glass which was lying on the floor from a broken window, and to use it to slash her wrists. He had then added: "It won't hurt; you will only feel cold for a short while."

Mrs Stevenson had heard enough. She grabbed hold of her daughter's hand and pulled her out of the accursed house.

The identity of the man in black remains a mystery.

THE BOY WITH X-RAY EYES

HAUNTED LIVERPOOL 4

This is a fascinating story which I unearthed from the old annals of the long-defunct, Lancashire Spiritualist Organisation. The human eye can only detect variations of black and white and the spectrum of just seven colours, but there have been many well-documented cases of people having eyes that are also sensitive to ultraviolet and infra-red light.

In 1920 in Liverpool, there lived an eleven-year-old boy called Peter Mills, who had begun to develop a very unusual faculty; he claimed that he could see right through solid objects, as if he had X-ray vision.

It all began when young Peter casually informed his shocked mother that his eldest sister, Patricia, had a little baby living inside her belly. Mrs Mills dismissed her son's strange claim as being the product of an over-active imagination and told him not to be so silly. However, she had to think again when, a week later, Patricia Mills eloped with a man almost twice her age from their street and later wrote home with the news that she was expecting his baby.

On another occasion, Mr Mills had a valuable pocket watch stolen during a wedding reception and young Peter swivelled around in his seat and started to scrutinise the bemused rows of guests. After a short time, the boy pointed towards Mr Mills' brother-in-law and accused him loudly and publicly of having the watch. The brother-in-law refused to empty his pockets to prove his innocence and a fight ensued. After the altercation, the defeated relative produced the stolen watch from his pocket, flung it at Peter's father and then stormed out of the reception.

Peter Mills' extraordinary powers were thoroughly tested by a professional magician and were declared to be genuine. The child could even detect what was written on a piece of paper which had been placed in a sealed, lead-lined box. He was also able to tell people what colour underwear they were wearing and also if they had had their appendix removed.

By 1929, his mysterious gift of X-ray vision slowly began to fade and, sadly, one of the last things Peter Mills managed to detect with his unique eyes, was a malignant tumour in his mother's breast, from which she died, not long afterwards.

LETTER FROM BEYOND THE GRAVE

In December 1923, the body of sixty-seven-year-old Mrs Heath lay in an open coffin in the front parlour of her home in Nevill Street, Southport. Wreaths of evergreens gemmed with roses lay in the hall, and upstairs in the bedroom, Moira, the forty-year-old daughter of the late Mrs Heath, was being comforted by her close and lifelong friend, Anthony. Moira was so beside herself with sorrow that, at the last minute, she couldn't bring herself to attend the funeral, so Anthony had told the other mourners that she would not be there and volunteered to stay behind and look after her.

As the hearse slowly carried the coffin away to the church, Moira and Anthony stood at the bedroom window, watching it turn the corner, then move slowly past the Coliseum Cinema, before disappearing into the depths of a swirling fog, followed by the entourage of mourners.

The house was hushed and empty now that the black-clad friends and relations had left, and Anthony and Moira sat before the blazing coals of a roaring fire in the drawing room, each sipping a sherry as they reflected on the life and personality of the deceased woman. Moira had mixed emotions about her dead mother – she had loved her dearly but resented her constant interference in her life. She told Anthony that if it hadn't been for her mother's constant interfering, she would still be married to Douglas, and would have had children around her now to comfort her in her hour of need. Alas, Mrs Heath had put such a strain on her daughter's relationship with Douglas, that he had divorced her fifteen years ago. Now she was left on the shelf, condemned to live alone for the rest of her life.

Moira was wallowing in self-pity when Anthony suddenly said, "Look, Moira, that's all water under the bridge now, love. You've got to get on with what's left of your life and make an effort to build a future for yourself."

"How can I, with so many awful memories? Mother has ruined my life!" she cried, starting to sniffle.

"Look, I know this might sound a little bizarre, but I was reading a book on psychology the other day, and the author mentioned this very interesting case ..." Anthony was saying, when he was interrupted.

"Not now, Anthony, please."

"Wait, Moira, please hear me out," Anthony went on. "A man blamed his mother for giving him some psychological complex which had blighted his life. I think she dressed him in girl's clothes when he was a child, or something similar. Anyhow, the psychiatrist told the man to write a letter to his mother asking him why she had given him a complex with her bizarre antics – even though the man's mother was dead."

Moira frowned.

"What good would that do if she was dead?"

"You see, just the act of writing the letter had some sort of therapeutic value to the man, and his complex gradually disappeared," Anthony explained.

"So, are you seriously suggesting that I should write a letter to my mother?" Moira asked.

Anthony took some time to persuade his bereaved friend to write the letter, but in the end she succumbed to his pressure, and that evening she sat at her late mother's Davenport writing desk, pouring her heart out on to the paper. Anthony sealed the letter and 'posted' it inside the Davenport's drawer. He advised Moira to now forget about the letter and to accompany him on a winter break to Scotland. Moira gladly took up the offer and thanked him profusely.

"You really are the dearest friend, Anthony. I really don't deserve your kindness."

And she smiled for the first time since her mother's death.

At Guthrie Castle, a week later, after a couple of stiff whiskeys, Anthony produced a ring and on his bended knee, shocked Moira with a proposal of marriage. He admitted that he had loved her for many years, but had been too shy to ask her to marry him before, for fear of rejection and the loss of her friendship. Moira accepted the proposal without any hesitation and flung her arms round him.

"Oh! Anthony! You are the most wonderful man I've ever met. Of course I'll marry you."

The newly-engaged couple arrived back at the house on Nevill Street, and some time later, Moira noticed an envelope on the Davenport writing desk when she was dusting in her mother's room. Inscribed upon it in a familiar script, were the words: 'To Moira'.

Moira opened the letter, and almost fainted as she scanned the contents of the letter. It was a reply to the letter she had written to her late mother. The

123

handwriting was without question that of her mother, and unfortunately, so too was the acidic, scathing prose. The author of the letter accused Moira of being a trollop, and claimed that Anthony had taken advantage of her during a time of crisis so that he could marry into her wealth.

'But not over my dead grave!' the letter ended.

Then a faint chuckling sound was heard nearby. Moira ran screaming downstairs and fled to Anthony's house. At first, Moira's fiancé thought the letter from beyond the grave was some kind of sick joke, but soon appreciated how deadly serious his fiancée was about the matter.

Whenever Anthony visited the house on Nevill Street, supernatural incidents would occur. A wine glass was hurled at him by some invisible hand, and on one occasion, when he fell asleep embracing Moira on the sofa, he was awakened by a pair of ice-cold hands trying to throttle him. Moira also caught fleeting glimpses of a woman in a long black dress wandering about at night in her bedroom, and could even detect the distinct aroma of the perfume her mother used to wear.

Shattered nerves eventually got the better of Moira and Anthony, and they ended up moving away from Moira's family home to Birkdale. When the wedding finally took place, not only did a substitute ring have to be used because the wedding band had vanished from the best man's pocket, but the interfering ghost of Mrs Heath even put in a personal appearance at the ceremony. This happened just as the priest was intoning that part of the marriage service which asks: "If any of you can show just cause why this couple may not lawfully be married, speak now, or else forever hold your peace."

An agonising shriek that seemed to originate in the transept echoed throughout the church. Some of those gathered for the ceremony later said that they had briefly seen a woman in black, shaking her fist at the couple, seemingly in protest at their union.

Fearing repercussions from the interfering ghost, Moira and Anthony subsequently moved even further away, to Ormskirk, and were troubled no more by the vindictive dead relative.

THE SHARED DREAM

In the 1970s in a certain area of Liverpool, a bully who can only be described as evil, was making the lives of a group of thirteen-year-old children a living hell. This was in an era when Child Line was undreamt of and when many uneducated parents would say to their bullied sons and daughters: "Give them a belt back, or they'll walk all over you."

But no one in their right mind would have considered hitting back at the bully who preyed on the younger pupils of a certain senior school in north Liverpool. We shall call the bully Mike.

At the age of fourteen Mike had already surpassed six feet in height, and now, at sixteen, in the final year of secondary school, he was filling out dramatically, probably on the chocolate bars and sweets he was forever seizing from his unfortunate victims. Like all bullies, Mike had surrounded himself with a group of sidekicks and fawning cronies, and even these pseudo-loyal followers came in for a severe beating now and then. Mike's father was an appalling role model, having been in and out of prison, on a regular basis, for most of his adult life, and his petite mum was completely cowed by her aggressive son.

What is more, things were getting worse of late. In a fit of temper, Mike had given his mother a black eye one day and wrung the neck of her budgerigar, simply because she had bought him the wrong brand of bottle-green flares. The police were brought in by Mike's fuming uncle but the bully's mother refused to testify against her son through a mixture of fear and love and claimed that the whole thing had been an accident; she had walked into a door. Mike and his gang wrecked his uncle's Cortina that night and sprayed 'GRASS' across the doors in silver paint.

One afternoon, in the school playground, Mike grabbed a timid, bespectacled thirteen-year-old boy named Philip by his ear and dragged him into the toilets where he snatched hold of his hair and started twisting it painfully. During this abduction, the cigar-chewing maths teacher on playground duty had been craftily distracted by two of Mike's lackeys, who had asked him to explain the difference between net and gross earnings. Meanwhile, in the toilets, Mike's right-hand man, Batesy, kept watch at the door, while Philip found himself shoved into a cubicle.

"Do you want to buy some looseys?" Mike asked, and produced a packet of Player's No. 6 cigarettes.

"I ... I ... d-d-don't smoke," stammered Philip, trying to keep the tremor out of his voice.

"Well then, you're just about to start. Okay, my little friend?"

Mike slid a cigarette out of the box and lit it with a golden Ronson lighter. He took a long drag on the filter tip and exhaled straight into Philip's face. Then he said, "Open your mush," and the boy opened his mouth without hesitation. He had seen too many heads cracked by Mike to even consider putting up any resistance. Mike thrust the cigarette into the boy's quivering mouth and ordered him to smoke it.

"Okay, Mike," Philip said, with the twitching cigarette apparently stuck to his lip. He puffed out smoke, and some of the exhalation accidentally went into Mike's eyes.

The bully let out a string of shocking pornographic-sounding expletives then shouted, "Smoke it properly, you stupid four-eyes! Breathe it in, you jessy!"

Philip had always had a weak chest and was probably asthmatic, and he started to cough and splutter, unable to catch his breath. In the panic of breathlessness he made the mistake of trying to push past Mike – and swiftly received a hard slap which knocked his spectacles down the toilet pan and made him see flashes of light, even though his eyes were closed tight.

The boy then stumbled and hit his ribs on the edge of the toilet seat, badly bruising his side. He looked up at the blurred image of the bully, then felt a sharp kick in the crotch which badly winded him and caused him to throw up all over the bully's shoes, and of course, this sent Mike into a frenzy. He tore a roll towel off its spindle with the intention of strangling Philip with it, but in the nick of time, the maths teacher arrived upon the scene after a tip-off from a young pupil who had heard the attack in the toilet.

"Get your hands off me, or I'll have you done in!" Mike bawled at the teacher as he seized his arm.

"Will you now, sonny?" smiled the teacher, who was a Fifth Dan Black Belt in Karate and was able to restrain Mike effortlessly. "You know something, I can't wait until you're expelled, lad," he said. "We don't want the likes of you in this school."

With that, he marched with him out of the toilets, where he instructed a caretaker to go and see if the kid in the cubicle was alright.

The headmaster visited Mike's mother at home and warned her once again about her son's totally unacceptable behaviour, and once again she told him how she herself had considered leaving home to get away from his violent ways. It was a no-win situation, no matter which way you looked at it.

The following Monday morning at 10.30pm, a thirteen-year-old boy was rushed from the playground into the medical room, bleeding profusely from his nose. This time Mike's gang had surrounded the boy in a scrum as the naive new English teacher had looked on, sipping a cup of tea as he patrolled the playground. "Boys will be boys," he thought, complacently. He was brought up with a start as the pupils began to disperse to reveal a child lying prostrate and inert on the cold macadam. That boy was Nick. It was he who had told the maths teacher about the beating his friend Philip was receiving from Mike on the Friday afternoon. Nick paid with a broken nose, and when he returned to school on the following day with a dressing on his face, he was too afraid to identify the culprits in the line-up. The headmaster unknowingly made things much worse by caning the three smirking members of Mike's gang anyway.

That day the torn-out page of an exercise book was placed in Philip's desk by someone while he was out in the playground. Upon that piece of paper, someone who couldn't spell had scrawled a chilling threat in block letters. It read: 'YOU WIL BE FOUND WHITH A NIFE IN YOUR BACK,' and this warning was accompanied by a drawing of a dagger dripping with blood.

When the bell rang an hour later, signifying the end of school for the day, Nick was getting ready to leave the classroom when he noticed that someone had slashed his blazer with a knife. He and Philip walked down the school corridor in trepidation, dreading the dark area beyond the self-closing doors that led to the gymnasium. Mike and his gang usually lurked there just by the exit, waiting to collar their victims. The two frightened boys loitered about in the corridor, hoping that the English teacher would accompany them, but instead he came out of the classroom whistling, seemingly oblivious to the boys' plight and went upstairs to chat to the female art teacher he was becoming quite fond of.

Nick and Philip decided to risk going out of the school by the exit on the other side of the building, but this proved to be a big mistake because Mike was waiting there with his deputy Batesy. The bully grabbed Nick by his tie.

"Oh look, Batesy!" he sneered. "It's little Nicholas ridiculous with the broken nose."

Batesy laughed, looked around, then grabbed Philip by the arm. He headbutted the boy, and watched as he sank to his knees, crying.

Nick was horrified. Then Mike told him what he could expect tomorrow.

"You know that acid tank in the metalwork room?"

Nick was too terrified even to nod.

"Well, your hand's going in there tomorrow," Mike promised with glee.

"Stop crying, you little Mary Ellen," said Batesy, looking down at the sobbing Philip.

The geography teacher heard the commotion and coming out of his classroom shouted, "Hey! What's going on?" from the far end of the corridor, but Mike and Batesy slipped away before he could reach them. The teacher asked Philip what the matter was, and the boy took his spectacles off and wiped away the tears.

"Nothing, sir."

"Who were those two boys who were here just now?" he asked, but Nick just shrugged and Philip said nothing, both fearing further reprisals if they gave the names of the bullies to the teachers.

On their way home from school, the boys decided that they needed to take a long walk in order to decide what to do. Nick said that they couldn't stay at the school any longer and suggested running away from home. He reminded Philip how, just a few weeks ago, Mike had been forced to abandon his attempt to dip another young pupil's hand in the tank of sulphuric acid in the metalwork room after the headmaster walked in unexpectedly. The boy had been held in a head-lock by Batesy, as Mike had been forcing the terrified boy's hand down towards the highly corrosive liquid. Days later, Mike's macabre fixation with the acid bath was satisfied when he snatched a first year boy's white pet mouse and lowered it into the tank by its tail. They both agreed that they were dealing with a madman who would stop at nothing once he'd got his teeth into you.

Philip then showed his friend the threatening note he had found in his desk, and that finally convinced Nick that the only way out was to run away from home. At that point something inside of Philip seemed to snap. He was blinking rapidly and looking into space with an expression of dread and didn't seem to know where he was.

"Phil!" shrieked Nick, grabbing the hood of his friend's parka and yanking him backwards, out of the path of a speeding car which narrowly missed him.

Philip seemed to be in a trance. He didn't even thank Nick for saving his life. Instead he said something very disturbing indeed.

"Nick, I'm going to murder Mike."

"You what?"

Nick was totally taken aback by this declaration. Philip was a gentle lad, he couldn't hurt a fly.

"My grandfather owns a gun, and I know where he keeps it," said Philip flatly.

He turned to his friend, and his eyes looked strange and empty, as if he was having a some kind of breakdown.

"Phil, don't talk like that," said Nick.

He shuddered because his friend certainly looked as if he had every intention of carrying out the threat. He said the words so coldly. It made Nick's flesh creep; this situation was getting way out of hand.

A lollipop man was walking down the pavement towards them and told the boys to cross with him further down the road.

"Don't even think of trying to stop me, Nick, because I'm in the mood to do something really bad, and if you stop me I'll kill myself, because I've had enough."

"Don't talk daft ... you can't ..." Nick glanced at the lollipop man, then whispered, "... go round shooting people, this isn't some stupid computer game. Stop it, Phil, you're scaring me."

That evening, Philip took Nick to his grandfather's flat, and as soon as the old man went out to the kitchen to make them a cup of tea, he sneaked into his room and came back holding an old Army service revolver. He briefly showed it to a horrified Nick, then stashed it in his satchel.

Later that night, Philip sat in Nick's bedroom, opening the chamber of the gun, just as he had seen his grandfather do so many times. It was loaded with five bullets. Nick pleaded with his friend not to go ahead with the planned murder, but Philip reminded him about the acid tank and the knife threat.

"You'll go to prison," Nick said, watching Philip roll the chambers.

"Only if they catch me, and they won't."

"The police aren't stupid, Phil. They will narrow it down to you and then there's your grandfather; he's going to know it's you when he sees the gun's been fired."

"They'll understand when I tell him how I was bullied," said Phil, and a lone tear, magnified by the lens of his spectacles, welled up and slid down his cheek.

"'Course they won't understand," said Nick, trying his utmost to dissuade his friend from committing the ultimate crime, "and you'll be a murderer."

Phil leaned forward and held his face in his right hand. His whole body was wracked with sobs, and the gun dangled limply from the other hand. Nick slowly reached out and took the weapon, and Philip put up no resistance whatsoever. He released the revolver, and Nick took it out of the room. He climbed the stairs and went up to the attic, where most of the junk of the house was chaotically stored. He removed a stack of documents from a biscuit tin and put the gun in there. He replaced the lid and then went back down to his friend, who had stopped crying and was now flipping through the pages of *Look-In* magazine.

"Let's go down and get something to eat," Nick said, and the two boys went down to the kitchen. Nick's mother had made a curry and the boys sat down and enjoyed their meals. Nick asked his mother if Phil could stay over, and she said he couldn't because it was a school night, but later relented. That night the boys slept top-tail in the bed, but they didn't fall asleep until almost 3am, because they were so worried about meeting Mike and Batesy in the morning.

Something very strange took place that morning at Nick's house. The boys experienced what is known as a 'shared dream', when two or more people have the very same dream. Some paranormal researchers who have catalogued such instances have hypothesised that the dream is shared telepathically by the dreaming minds. Whatever the true cause, Philip and Nick awoke at 8 o'clock that morning to a ringing alarm clock suffused with a peaceful feeling, which they couldn't explain, given the serious bullying problems they were both having to contend with. Neither of them could work out why, but they felt no fear or apprehension about the prospect of going to school.

At the breakfast table, Nick said, "I had a weird dream last night about that Mike."

"So did I," said Philip, through a mouthful of toast.

"I dreamt he was lying in this bed and a woman was saying 'Get up!' and he wouldn't get up," said Nick.

Philip's jaw dropped, for the exact same thing had happened in his dream. Nick found this hard to believe, until Philip went on to tell him how the dream ended.

"The woman started screaming really loudly, and that really scared me. She looked insane, and she started to shake Mike, and then the room went all black."

Nick turned to his bemused mother, who had little knowledge of the traumatic trials her son was going through at the hands of Mike and his cohorts. She had believed her son when he had told her that his swollen nose was the result of some innocent rough and tumble in the playground.

"Both of you can't have had the same dream," she laughed, drawing on her mundane common sense.

"But that's just it, we did," Nick said, and he and Philip looked at one another with baffled expressions.

In the school assembly hall, Nick and Philip and a majority of the pupils noticed that Mike was absent and the communal sense of relief was almost palpable. The staff on the stage seemed to be in a very solemn mood for some reason and then the headmaster walked in and stood at the front row, gravely surveying the assembled school. He asked everyone to be quiet in an unusually soft voice, then asked the pupils to sit down. Choosing his words very carefully, he then told everyone the tragic news about the death of one of the school's pupils. Apparently, Mike had been found dead in his bed early that morning. The cause of death wasn't known, but later on, in the local newspapers, that rather vague term 'natural causes' was mentioned. The article also described how Mike's mother – unable to accept his sudden death – had tried desperately to shake her son awake on his deathbed before her hysterical screams brought her neighbours running to the house.

Nick and Philip felt cold shivers when they read the newspaper piece, and instantly recalled the weird dream they had both shared. Nick admitted that on the night when they had shared that dream, just before he fell asleep, he had prayed to God, asking him to somehow stop the bullies at the school. Was the resulting shared dream and the sudden death of Mike some strange coincidence, or were Nick's prayers answered?

Batesy lost no time in trying to take over from Mike, but was expelled from the school after he was caught red-handed holding a pupil's head down a toilet. The culture of bullying soon ended after Batesy's departure. Nick and Philip began to look forward to attending school after that dark period, and both lads ended up going to university.

BACK ON TRACK

A calm cold night had fallen on the city of Liverpool. High above the haze of the factory smoke-stacks in the north, a full moon shone down on the night of Tuesday, 24 May 1910. Even the brilliance of the lunar orb was not sufficiently bright to blot out that mysterious ghost from the depths of time and space – Halley's Comet. The vaporous interplanetary wanderer hung stretched out in the starry arched heavens near the constellations of Gemini and Leo.

This was the twenty-ninth recorded visit of the great celestial apparition, and in her time she had looked down many times each century to witness the rise and fall of civilisations and the tardy advancement of mankind, from the days of prehistory to the building of the pyramids, from the beginnings of the Roman Empire to the French Revolution.

Upon this occasion, however, the long-tailed comet looked down on a truly pitiful sight; dozens of homeless and discarded mortals, sleeping, hunched up under thin sheets of newspaper, in the parks of the city at midnight. Perhaps a few of these unfortunate men, women and children stirred from their alfresco slumbers and caught a glimpse of the visiting comet before pulling the newspaper blankets over their faces and sinking back into the happier world of their dreams.

Elsewhere in Liverpool, a policeman strolling on his measured beat was regularly eyeing the unfamiliar smudge of light in the night sky, and a few of those privileged enough to be sleeping under a roof took a thoughtful gaze at the comet through their bedroom windows before the candle was blown out.

Ethel Godwinson, a frail sixty-year-old widow, was amongst this latter group. She gazed from her bedroom window at the spectral comet in the western sky and thought about all of the panic it had engendered. She was an avid reader of the newspapers, and had read every scare-mongering article on Comet Halley. Astronomers had apparently detected poisonous cyanogen gas in the spectrum of the comet's tail and it had been predicted that the Earth would pass through it.

Fortunately, the nucleus of the comet had only approached within thirteen million miles of Earth, yet the world in its orbit had actually passed through the outer portion of Halley's tail. Luckily for the human race, the cyanogen gas had been so tenuous, that it had posed no threat to the planet.

Mrs Godwinson dwelt for a while on the unfathomable scale of outer space, the origin of the universe and the meaning of existence, before turning in for the night. She was on the brink of falling asleep when she distinctly heard a noise on the landing outside her bedroom door. As she lived alone, she knew it had to be an intruder, and she trembled in her bed. Sure enough, the door slowly creaked open, and the shadowy form of a stout man entered. Mrs Godwinson let out a stifled yelp, but in a heartbeat the fellow was upon her, holding the blade of a clasp knife to her throat.

"You make even a peep and you're dead!" he warned, in a distinctive Northern Irish accent.

Mrs Godwinson's late neighbour, old Mr McKay, had spoken in the exact same accent, being raised in Belfast, so she recognised it at once. She started to cry. The moonlight filtering in through the drawn curtains shone on the man's knife-wielding hand. That hand had half of its forefinger missing. The other hand pressed down hard on her bosom, and across the knuckles slithered the tattoo of a snake. A handkerchief covered the bottom half of the knifeman's face, and the peaked cloth cap he wore cast a shadow over the remaining half. He ordered the terrified widow to get out of bed, and he seemed to know all about the small wooden chest that was hidden under the bed and which contained the five hundred pounds of Mrs Godwinson's life savings. Kicking her viciously in the ribs, he ordered her to drag the chest out. Cringing from the blows, she pulled it out and he ordered her to open it.

The overweight thug was soon stuffing the money into his pockets, and Mrs Godwinson felt some relief – at least her ordeal would soon be over now that he had got what he wanted. Not a bit of it! The burglar started slapping her hard across the face, and warned her that if she tried to raise the alarm after he had left, he'd come back and slit her throat. He then left the bedroom.

The police were not contacted until the following morning, when the bruised and battered widow finally dared to venture out of her bedroom. Not only had the nine-and-a-half fingered thief taken all her savings, he had also stolen her jewellery, which had been kept in a velvet-lined box in a cabinet in the parlour. Amongst the jewellery was a distinctive gold St Christopher's medal which had been in her family for generations.

Ethel's thirty-five-year-old son Michael swore he would somehow track down the cowardly burglar who had reduced his frail widowed mother to a nervous wreck. Ethel suffered terrible nightmares about the burglar, and would wake up screaming in the night.

The police knew of no one in the underworld who matched the man's description, and as the weeks went by, no progress was made by the detectives on the case.

In the July of that year, just two months after the robbery, a curious coincidence took place. A priest visited Ethel Godwinson's Everton home, and during the long conversation he had with the widow, he told of an old superstition associated with St Christopher – the saint featured on the medal which the burglar had stolen. Years ago, in Ireland, when people wanted to find money that had been lost or stolen, they'd say: "Saint Christopher, Saint Christopher, return that which is rightly mine!" After uttering this, a reversal of the misfortune would take place, and the missing or stolen items would soon be recovered. This was because Saint Christopher was the patron saint of lost causes and mislaid objects.

Mrs Godwinson duly recited the saint's name twice over and asked for her savings and jewellery to be returned. She had no faith that the incantation would work, but she recited it more for the sake of the priest than anything else. This all took place at half-past one in the afternoon.

At that precise time, a short but broad and muscular man in a cloth cap entered the dark warren of shops and offices at Tuton Chambers, 44 Lime Street, and walked upstairs to a tattooing studio. The man was Rory Kavanagh, and he told the tattoo artist precisely what he wanted in a raw Northern Irish accent. Kavanagh wanted a picture of a naked woman lying stretched out across his back. The Irishman pointed to the framed drawing of the woman in question hanging on the wall. When he pointed at her, he pointed with only half a forefinger. The tattoo artist – Michael Godwinson – also noticed the writhing green serpent tattooed across the knuckles of the man's other hand.

When Kavanagh stripped to the waist, Michael instantly noticed the distinctive oversized Saint Christopher medal hanging on a chain from his neck. He recognised it immediately as the one stolen from his mother, and the man wearing it was the very brute who had held the knife to her throat that night in May. Michael Godwinson managed to keep calm on the outside, but beneath the composed exterior, he was seething and had to suppress a strong desire to batter the Irishman's head in. Instead of which, he exacted a very unusual revenge upon the robber.

Instead of tattooing a naked lady upon Kavanagh's fleshy back, Michael Godwinson used his needles to inscribe, in capital letters, the sentence, 'I AM A THIEF AND A WOMAN BEATER' in a very aesthetic-looking font, straight across the Irishman's back. After Michael had finished the last letter, he made an excuse to leave the room and he called for a policeman. Kavanagh was subsequently arrested, and although he had already spent a quarter of Mrs Godwinson's life-savings, the rest of the money and most of the jewellery was recovered, along with an extensive collection of loot from some of Kavanagh's other cowardly crimes.

Rory Kavanagh was given twelve years' hard labour for his crimes, and for the rest of his life, he carried the tattooed words of shame on his back.

A STONY EMBRACE

This is a particularly eerie mystery that allegedly took place in Liverpool during the severe winter of 1962. That year, fifteen-year-old Nancy Greenwell of Dovecot was introduced to Robert Jones by her cousin. Robert lived in Ince Avenue, and it became a regular occurrence for him to take Nancy round to his friend's house almost every night. As the couple started courting, Nancy became completely obsessed with Robert. She used to scribble his name on her exercise books at school, talk incessantly about him all day long and would spend all her pocket money on him, plying him with records and other gifts. Robert's father soon insisted that his son should get a job instead of wasting his time just lounging about with Nancy. Hostility built up between them and in the end he warned Robert never to bring the girl home again.

As an act of rebellion against his strict parents, Robert and Nancy started mixing with a local gang. They used to wander around Anfield Cemetery, amusing themselves in the dusky evenings. One evening, Nancy was on the bus going to a friend's house, when she saw something that shattered her heart. As the bus was travelling up Queen's Drive, she happened to glance out of the window and, just as she did so, she saw Robert, in a bus shelter, locked in a passionate embrace with her best friend, Tina.

In a state of shock, Nancy remained firmly seated on the bus as the tears started to flow. When she reached her stop, she got off and wandered around in a complete daze. Robert's friend saw her walking into Anfield Cemetery looking very forlorn. The distressed girl was next seen by a school friend named Maureen Davies. Nancy was very emotional as she told Maureen what had just happened. In near hysterics, she exclaimed that she wanted to die, before running off between a row of gravestones.

It was getting late and was now extremely dark. Inside the tree-framed cemetery, away from the streetlamps, it was almost pitch black, and Maureen was too frightened to carry on looking for her friend. She left hastily, and made her way round to Nancy's parents, where she informed them that their daughter had seemed devastated by what she had seen and looked almost suicidal. They were obviously deeply concerned, and became increasingly worried when

Nancy had still not returned home by eleven o'clock that night. They alerted the police, who searched the deserted cemetery, but Nancy Greenwell was nowhere to be found. Then the beam of a policeman's torch flitted over something curious in the distance as he was on his way out of the vast necropolis. There before him, was a huge, white, marble statue of a man, about nine feet in height, with its arms stretched out before it. Draped across the arms of this imposing figure was the limp body of Nancy Greenwell.

That night, temperatures had plunged to five degrees below zero, and the post-mortem established that the girl had died from hypothermia; yet how she had ended up in the arms of the statue was never solved. Then came another mystery. The statue of the stone man had no inscription on it and, after a thorough investigation, it was established that it had never been part of any grave or memorial. There were no records of who had erected it, and consequently it was eventually removed by the Parks and Gardens Department.

It later came to light that people in the Anfield area regarded the unidentified statue as having a supernatural reputation, and some seriously alleged that the marble figure had actually been seen to move on several occasions. Its last resting place was a private garden in Tudor Court, on the campus of Liverpool University, facing the University Baths on Oxford Street.

One night, in 1975, that nine foot marble statue vanished into thin air. Its present whereabouts, and its role in the death of Nancy Greenwell in 1962, remain a mystery to date.

THE WITCH DOCTOR'S CURSE

HAUNTED LIVERPOOL 4

In the eighteenth century, the City of Liverpool became prosperous through the so-called 'ships of shame', which transported millions of black African slaves to America and the West Indies. The rapidly-growing colonies of the New World were in need of a massive labour force and the vile businessmen of England thought that the black men, women and children of Africa, could fulfil the demand for workers. Around ten million African slaves were shipped across the Atlantic in appalling conditions. Each slave was confined to a space in the ship's hold which had less room than a coffin. They were shackled to one another and therefore had to wallow in each other's dirt for months on end. Not surprisingly, fever, dysentery and a high mortality rate were commonplace on the slave ships during the hazardous voyage from Africa to the western side of the Atlantic. Sick and dying slaves were regarded as a dead loss to the slave-sellers, so many of the Africans who were suspected of being ill were thrown overboard, to drown or be eaten by the sharks.

In November 1781, a Captain Collingwood, of the slave ship *Zong*, ordered his men to take turns in throwing 133 slaves into the ocean. Only a few of the poor souls jettisoned into the shark-infested waters were ill, but Captain Collingwood thought the cruel measure would be an effective way of conserving the ship's fresh water reservoir, which was running low. Against this evil backdrop of extreme cruelty and total disregard for human life, the following strange tale unfolded.

It began in the year 1783, when a Liverpool slave ship, the *Amelia*, picked up its captured human cargo from the port of Old Calabar in Nigeria. Among the men, women and children who had been abducted and taken by force from their country, was a young boy of thirteen named Abu and his uncle, Obah, a partially blind, grey-haired, old man who, curiously, knew a little English. During the *Amelia's* voyage to the West Indies, Abu suffered a fit and Obah appealed to the crew for water. The old man's frantic request fell on deaf ears and so he, and a number of other slaves down in the hold, started to rattle their chains in protest.

The ship's master, Captain Mallard, was enraged by their actions and had the protesting slaves brought up on deck, where they were subjected to lengthy flogging sessions. Abu, despite being ill, was also flogged and fainted as a result. His uncle threw himself over the boy and begged the captain to give him some water. Obah struggled to explain who the boy was and, through an interpreter, revealed that young Abu was prone to strange fits which gave him visions. The child was the only son of his tribe's witch-doctor and he warned that if he was not taken back to Nigeria, a terrible curse would fall upon the captain of the *Amelia*.

When Captain Mallard heard this, he grabbed the boy by his ankles and started to swing him viciously around. The boy screamed and his elderly uncle tried to attack the captain. Suddenly, Mallard let go of the child and he shot headfirst over the ship's rail and plunged into the waves beneath. There was an uproar of protest from the slaves below deck who had witnessed the captain's cowardly and callous act and angry eyes, bursting with hatred, stared up through the slits in the deck's barricado.

Old Obah sobbed and was promptly bundled down into the hold and chained up again. As the shackles were put on him, the old man pointed an accusing finger at Captain Mallard and hissed out the following words:

"Curse you! Curse you, Captain, and all your family!"

Ten months later, all the slaves from the *Amelia* had been sold; all except the half-blind slave, Obah. Old slaves were almost impossible to sell and ones who could hardly see, could not even be given away. Obah, therefore, was taken to Liverpool and offered to anyone who would have him. He was put on exhibition on the steps of the Liverpool Custom House and was adopted by a well-to-do couple from the Calderstones district of Liverpool, named George and Catherine Hughes. The couple looked after Obah, until he died ten years later from a fever.

Not long after Captain Mallard's return to the port of Liverpool, bad luck and weird occurrences started to haunt him and his family. His eldest son, Matthew, who had a cottage overlooking the shore at Formby, went insane after telling his wife that an enormous black dog, with glowing red eyes, had stalked him during his evening walk through the sand dunes. He claimed that the hound was jet black and left no tracks in the sand as it chased after him. Matthew's wife watched him disintegrate into a shambling nervous wreck over the next few days and ended up deserting him. The poor fellow was later committed to a lunatic asylum.

Weeks later, Captain Mallard was awakened, in the middle of the night, at his Duke Street home, when he heard a strange drum beating in the distance. Even his neighbours heard the strange thumping sound, but no one could tell where the noise was coming from. Three nights later, the infuriating rhythm of the drum ceased abruptly at precisely 4.15am and Captain Mallard later learned that his elderly mother, in Frederick Street, had died at that exact time after screaming out just once in her sleep.

A month later, the same eerie drumbeat disturbed the sleep of Captain Mallard once more. This time he awoke in his four-poster bed to find his wife lying in a pool of blood beside him. She had suffered a life-threatening miscarriage and almost died as a result.

Then something chilling took place one Sunday, after Mallard had been entertaining a Captain Slater at his Duke Street home. Mrs Mallard found a strange object on the mantelpiece of the drawing room. At first she thought it was a doll's head but when she picked it up and inspected it, she found that it was too lifelike and had a hideous, putrid quality about it. She screamed in horror and flung it into the fire. Captain Mallard retrieved the loathesome thing from the glowing coals with a pair of tongs and discovered, to his horror, that it was the shrivelled head of a real human being. It was one of the so-called shrunken heads, which are allegedly used by shamans and witch-doctors as a black magic talisman. Mallard thought Captain Slater had planted the head in his drawing room, but Slater swore that he had never set eyes on it before.

Mrs Vaughan, the maid-of-all-work in the Mallard household, later reported hearing the sound of the strange drum once again and said that she had been having vivid nightmares featuring a black man's grinning face, painted with white stripes.

Captain Mallard decided to go back to sea in an attempt to escape from the ghostly goings-on at his Duke Street home. He captained a vessel called the *Moonrise* which was bound for Littleton, in New Zealand. He was to bring back a consignment of wool and frozen mutton from New Zealand, but his ship later vanished without a trace.

Twenty-six years later, a British ship called the *Horizon* caught sight of a large sailing vessel drifting off the coast of Chile. As the ship drew nearer, the crew of the *Horizon* could see that the vessel was apparently unmanned but, stranger still, the masts and ragged sails of the ship were covered with thick deposits of a green mould. On the prow, faded with the weather and the passage of time, the crew of the *Horizon* could make out the name, *Moonrise*.

A boarding party from the *Horizon* investigated the apparently abandoned ship and when one of the crew jumped on to the deck, the timbers had decayed to such an extent that they crumbled beneath him. The other men hauled their colleague out of the hole and proceeded cautiously around the deck. In the captain's cabin, a skeleton in ragged clothes was discovered and the atmosphere was pervaded by an intense smell of decay. A further thirteen skeletons were found elsewhere on the *Moonrise*. They had all presumably died from some sickness long ago. The *Horizon's* captain inspected the damp, mouldy pages of the ship's log-book to examine the last entries, but the ink had become too blurred by moisture to be legible.

Suddenly, a loud groaning noise echoed down the length of the *Moonrise*, followed by a loud crack. The captain and his men hastened on to the deck and watched in horror as the main mast crashed down into the waters. In a state of panic, the men rushed back to the lifeboat and rowed frantically towards their own ship. As the boat moved away, the ship with the crew of skeletons started to break up. The remaining two masts toppled on to the decks of the *Moonrise* and, within seconds, the rotting hulk started to sink at the stern. The *Horizon* crew managed to row away just in time to avoid being sucked down with the rapidly-sinking vessel.

When news of the strange discovery of the long-lost ship reached the ears of Captain Mallard's wife, who was now in her sixties, she passed out with the shock. She falteringly informed the doctor that her husband had been cursed to death for killing a witch doctor's son, before becoming incoherent. The doctor administered laudanum but Mrs Mallard broke out in a sweat and her eyes rolled about. At the moment of her death, at 3 o'clock in the morning, seven people attending her sickbed heard the howl of a dog out in the street.

The strange tale was reported in the local newspaper and when Mr and Mrs Hughes – the couple who had looked after the old slave, Obah, and knew about the curse – read about the discovery of Captain Mallard's old ship and the ensuing sudden death of his wife, they felt certain that the witch doctor's curse had done its work.

THE STORY OF SPRING-HEELED JACK

In Victorian times, Barnes Common, an isolated tract of land on the southern bank of the Thames, was a place to avoid. Travellers foolhardy enough to cross the common during twilight hours, were often attacked and robbed.

One evening, in 1837, a businessman, who had been working overtime at his office, decided to risk a short cut across the common on his way home, when a figure suddenly vaulted high over the railings of the cemetery – as if propelled from a springboard – and landed with a thud in front of him. The businessman turned and fled when he noticed that the mysterious leaper had pointed ears, glowing eyes and a prominent pointed nose.

Three girls encountered the same sinister figure the following night. Again, he made his appearance by bounding over the railings of the cemetery but, on this occasion, he displayed a violent streak. One of the girls had her coat ripped as he passed by her, but she managed to flee, closely followed by one of her screaming companions. The third girl tried to scream as the unearthly-looking stranger grabbed at her breasts and began tearing off her clothes, before leaving her unconscious.

During the following month, the leaping terror struck again. This time the venue was Cut-Throat Lane, Clapham Common. After visiting her parents in Battersea, Mary Stevens, a servant, headed back to her employer's household on Lavender Hill. As she strolled through the entrance of Cut-Throat Lane, a tall figure, dressed in black, jumped out of the darkness and threw his arms around her, holding her in a vice-like embrace. Before she had a chance to scream, the stranger kissed her face, then dipped his hand into her cleavage, before laughing hysterically. The girl screamed and the stranger released her and ran off into the darkness.

A number of men hurried to the aid of the distressed girl and, after calming her down, they listened to her account of the attack. The men immediately searched the neighbourhood for the mysterious assailant, but without success. The following night, the attacker appeared again, not a stone's throw from the house where the servant girl worked.

That night, the demonic figure bounded out of the shadows into the path of an approaching carriage. The horses pulling the carriage bolted in fright and a terrible crash ensued, injuring the coachman. The mayhem-maker then seemed to defy the laws of gravity, as he jumped effortlessly over a nine-foot high wall. Not long after that superhuman feat, a mysterious high-jumping man with a cape attacked a woman near Clapham churchyard.

Gradually, the news of the satanic superman spread and the public gave him a name – Spring-Heeled Jack. In February 1838, eighteen-year-old Lucy Scales, and her sister Margaret, were on their way home in the evening, after visiting their brother's house in the Limehouse area.

Suddenly, the terrifying cloaked silhouette of Spring-Heeled Jack leapt out of the darkness and exhaled a jet of blue flames, from his mouth, straight into Lucy's face. The teenager screamed, her legs collapsed under her and she fell to the ground, blinded. Jack jumped high over his victim and her sister, landed on the roof of a house and bounded off into the night.

A pattern was emerging. Jack seemed to enjoy molesting and terrifying young females. His next attack, which took place two days later, was also on an eighteen-year-old girl, Jane Alsop. Jane's house was in Bearhind Lane, a quiet back street in the district of Bow, where she lived with her father and two sisters. She was spending the evening reading when, just before 9 o'clock, there was a knock on the front door. Jane answered and outside in the shadows stood a caped man. He said to Jane, "I'm a policeman. Bring a light! We've caught Spring Heeled Jack in the lane!" Jane ran excitedly back into the house and returned with a candle. Offering the candle to the caller, she beheld a nightmarish sight. The flickering light illuminated the face of the man purporting to be an officer of the law. It was Jack and he grinned as he studied the girl's shocked expression.

Before she could move, he spurted out a phosphorescent gas, which partially blinded Jane, then started tearing at her clothes. She punched his big nose and managed to give him the slip but the enraged Jack bolted after her and stopped her from re-entering the house by clutching her hair. His claw-like hands scraped her face and neck but Jane's screams alerted her sisters, who came running out of the house and they managed to drag her from her attacker. The three sisters retreated indoors, with Spring-Heel in hot pursuit and, in the nick of time, the door was slammed in Jack's face.

When Jane was quizzed by the Lambeth Police Court about the assailant's appearance, she described a very unusual person:

143

"He wore a large helmet and a tight-fitting costume that felt like oilskin. But the cape was just like the ones worn by policemen. His hands were as cold as ice and like powerful claws. But the most frightening thing about him was his eyes. They shone like balls of fire."

Two days later, Jane's description was strengthened by the testimony of a butcher from Limehouse. He was the brother of Lucy and Margaret Scales – the victims of the Green Dragon Alley attack.

Accounts of Spring-Heeled Jack's cowardly assaults on the ladies of South London soon spread, scaring many into staying indoors after dark, while others decided to organise vigilante patrols.

A week after the attack on Jane Alsop, Jack called at a house in Turner Street, off Commercial Road. A servant boy answered the door, and Jack, shielding half of his face with his cloak as he stood in the shadows, asked the boy if he could talk to the master of the house. The youngster was turning, about to call for the master, when Jack made the mistake of moving out of the shade into the lamplight. The boy recoiled in horror when he saw that the caller had bright orange eyes. As he stood there in a state of shock, he noticed two other details about the mysterious caller; he had claws for hands and, under his cloak, an intricate embroidered design that resembled a coat of arms with, below this design, the letter 'W' embroidered in gold. The boy had heard all the spine-chilling rumours of Jack's 'eyes of Hell'. He let out a terrific scream and, within seconds, windows and doors all over the neighbourhood were opening. Jack waved his fist threateningly at the boy, then rocketed over the roofs of Commercial Road.

When the boy regained his senses, he was cross-questioned and interrogated repeatedly by the authorities about his hair-raising encounter. His inquisitors wondered what the significance of the embroidered 'W' was and some conjectured that it was the initial of the Marquis of Waterford, widely known as a mischievous prankster. The Marquis was also something of an athlete, but his physical capabilities could obviously not be equated with Jack's superhuman stunts. Even the fittest man on earth could not leap twenty-five feet into the air, as Jack was alleged to have done many times. In 1859, the Marquis met his death after falling from a horse but the reports of the 'Jack' continued to pour into London police stations and newspaper offices. Spring-Heeled Jack was still at large.

He made an appearance in Lincolnshire one evening, where he shattered the rural tranquillity by leaping over thatched cottages wearing a sheepskin. A mob confronted the laughing leaper and blasted him with shotguns at point-blank range but their firepower had no effect. When the buckshot hit Jack, it sounded as if it was hitting a metal bucket.

One night, in January 1879, a man driving his cart across a bridge on the Birmingham and Liverpool Junction Canal on his way home from Woodcote, Shropshire, was startled when a black, hideous creature, with large luminous eyes, leapt out of a tree and landed on the horse's back. The man tried to knock the beast off the horse with his whip but the creature managed to hold on to the frightened animal, which broke into a wild gallop. When the man got the cart back under control, the 'thing' darted high into the air and disappeared into the trees.

By the end of the nineteenth century, the geographical pattern of sightings of Spring-Heeled Jack indicated that he was moving in a westerly direction across England, towards Lancashire. In September 1904, the blackguard turned up in Liverpool, where he was seen hurtling down from the roof of High Park Street reservoir. Soon afterwards, Jack gave a typical performance when he was seen clinging to the steeple of St Francis Xavier's in Salisbury Street. Before the awe-struck crowds filling the streets below, Jack jumped suicidally from the steeple and landed somewhere behind a row of houses. The mobs stampeded to see where he had landed and a rumour spread that he had killed himself. The Evertonians were subsequently startled when a helmeted, egg-headed figure in white, suddenly ran down the street towards them. As several women in the crowd screamed, Jack lifted his arms and flew over William Henry Street. After that memorable night, Jack made himself scarce for sixteen years.

Then, late one evening in 1920, a man dressed in a radiant-white costume, was seen by scores of witnesses in Warrington's Horsemarket Street, jumping back and forth from the pavements to the rooftops. He finally cleared the town's railway station in one mighty leap and was never seen in the north of England again.

In 1948, the last recorded sighting of a sinister leaping figure, took place at Monmouth in South Wales. Locals who saw a strange-looking man leaping over a stream near Watery Lane, surmised that he was the spectre of a man who had drowned in the stream but the few Welsh folk who were unfortunate enough to encounter the leaper at close quarters, swore that he was too solid to be a phantom.

Who or what was Spring-Heeled Jack? Many bizarre theories have been advanced to answer the question. Some said he was an insane acrobatic fire-eater, others believed him to be a dressed-up kangaroo, or a mad inventor who had built an anti-gravity device. One theory that does fit the facts is the alien hypothesis. If we suppose that Jack was from another planet, this would explain his alien appearance, behaviour, jumping ability and longevity.

The descriptions of Spring-Heeled Jack's fiery gaze seem to indicate that he had retro-reflective eyes, similar to a cat, which would suggest he was ideally suited to a nocturnal environment. His fire-breathing is not easily explained. Perhaps what Jack really breathed into his victims eyes was not real fire (for none of those attacked suffered burns, nor did the 'fire' ever singe a single hair), but a type of phosphor.

Another unanswered riddle is the fate of Jack. If he was a misunderstood alien, marooned in our world, was he finally rescued, or did he die a lonely death here? We will probably never know.

THE REAL JEKYLL AND HYDE

HAUNTED LIVERPOOL 3

Most people have heard or read of Robert Louis Stevenson's disturbing tale of dual personality, *The Strange Case of Dr Jekyll and Mr Hyde*, which was first published in 1886. Some think that Stevenson based his story on the double life of Edinburgh's Deacon Brodie, who was a respectable businessman by day and a vicious thief by night. But there was also a real-life Jekyll and Hyde character at large in Liverpool in the mid-nineteenth century.

Richard Rawlins was a fairly wealthy engineer who had shares in several Cornish tin mines as well as the Liverpool to Manchester Railway. He was said to be a tall, dark, handsome man with a fine voice and a rather shrewd nature. He had married three times, each marriage ending after a year because of Rawlins' dramatic mood swings and strange dual personality.

From his childhood, Richard Rawlins claimed that he had a naughty 'twin' inside him named Ralph. The young child even changed hands to write and draw when he became Ralph. Ralph was a nasty, mischievous personality who delighted in pulling the legs off spiders and Richard was a nice boy who picked flowers for his mother. It was Richard's mother who had unwittingly christened Richard's 'twin', after her son had told her about the imaginary double who lived inside him. Richard called his alter ego 'the other fellow', but Mrs Rawlins suggested the name Ralph, which had been her grandfather's name.

A children's doctor was baffled at the child's split personality disorder and surmised it was just young Richard's way of getting attention. However, in adolescence, Richard became Ralph more often, usually when he had undergone an emotional time or had been involved in an accident.

When sixteen-year-old Richard broke up with his girlfriend Lottie, he broke down in tears in Toxteth Park. A policeman approached the distressed young man and asked him what was the matter. The rejected Romeo's angelic face became twisted and his eyes squinted at the police officer. Richard had become Ralph and he spat in the policeman's face and ran out of the park shouting abuse at passers-by. Upon reaching his home in Duke Street, the mentally unstable teenager was attacked by his dog Samson, a huge black Labrador. The dog loved Richard but growled and ran from the boy when he 'became' Ralph.

The teenager ran into the front parlour and suffered a fit. He was found by the maid, biting into the hearth rug and foaming at the mouth. As the maid called for Richard's father, the fit subsided and he passed out. When he was revived with smelling salts, he told his parents that Ralph had spat at a policeman and had screamed abuse at people in the street on his way home.

The weeks went by without Ralph appearing and the boy seemed normal enough in other respects. Only occasionally did he swap his pen to his left hand when he wrote and even then there were only minor variations in the teenager's handwriting style. As the years passed, it looked as if the rebellious Ralph had disappeared forever into the depths of Richard Rawlins' subconscious. But in 1845, a dramatic accident brought Ralph racing back into Richard's life with a vengeance.

Richard Rawlins was now a twenty-five-year-old mining engineer who patented several explosive devices for blasting quarries and mines. On 1 November 1845, Rawlins entered the Dale Street premises of Rodney Hart, a gunsmith and gunpowder supplier. Rawlins intended to purchase five pounds of gunpowder to test out a detonation device he was working on for the mines. Whilst he was there, a young apprentice in the cellar of the shop dropped a flintlock he had just loaded and the gun went off, blasting a hole in a barrel of gunpowder. The apprentice was killed instantly and only parts of his body were ever recovered. The shop-owner Rodney Hart was blown through the windows of the premises but survived. Richard Rawlins was blown up on to the first floor of the devastated shop by the tremendous force of the blast. He was found hanging over a beam, barely alive, suffering from concussion.

He was treated at his Duke Street home by several distinguished physicians from a Rodney Street surgery and, for a week, it looked as if the young man would remain in a permanent comatose state. Amazingly, he pulled through or, at least, Ralph pulled through, because Richard's personality was evidently destroyed in the shop explosion.

As soon as the young man was able to get out of his bed, he practically raped his maid and then sexually assaulted the cook who was a sixty-year-old woman. Ralph stole over one hundred guineas from his father's room and then escaped by climbing dangerously out of a garret window. He ran across the rooftops and went on a crime spree, committing two burglaries in the Islington district, sexually assaulting three young women in Everton and almost battering a pub landlord to death because the ale he served was slightly sour.

Unlike the meek Richard, Ralph had the strength of a savage beast and seemed to take delight in battling with the police. The wayward Ralph Rawlins was finally cornered in Vauxhall Road a week later by eight policemen armed with batons. The mixed-up young man had just set fire to a soap warehouse and the damage was estimated to be almost one thousand pounds.

Sadly, a blow on the skull from a policeman's riot baton killed Ralph instantly. The man with two personalities suffered a haemorrhage of the brain and died with blood gushing from his nose and ears. Surgeons at the Liverpool Medical Institute in Mount Pleasant were eager to get to the bottom of the dead man's double personality and sought permission to open up his skull. At first Ralph's father refused permission, but later had a change of heart, as he too was curious to learn about his son's illness.

A surgeon sawed open the skull of the young man and was flabbergasted by what he saw: there were two brains tightly pressed together in the skull case, or four hemispherical lobes in all. The surgeon surmised that Richard was meant to have been one half of a twin when he was conceived. The other twin never developed into an embryo but retained its brain, which grew alongside the brain of its twin.

Undoubtedly, one of the brains contained the personality of Richard and the other brain was the spiteful counterpart which asserted itself as Ralph. The Rawlins family naturally did not want society to know of their freakish son, so the findings of the Medical Institute were filed away for posterity.

BLACK MARY

Over the years I have heard many ghost stories about the restless phantom of 'Black Mary', a shadowy apparition of a woman who roams St George's Hall. From my own researches, and from several reliable accounts about the spectre from people working at St George's Hall, I have managed to piece together the following:

Around 1989, in a window in a Bold Street shop that sold fine art, I once saw a beautiful oil painting by an obscure Lancashire artist from the Victorian period, William Osbert. Set in what was said to be Sefton Park, the subject of the painting was a palm reader who looked like the archetypal female gypsy of popular imagination, complete with the colourful headscarf and large gold loop earrings. Her face was dark, her green eyes large and mysterious, and surrounding the Romany mystic was a circle of well-to-do bonneted ladies carrying parasols. One of these upper class women was having her palm read by the gypsy woman. The title of the work was 'Palm-reading Sunday'. It was dated 1873, the year after the park had been officially opened by Prince Arthur. I inquired about the background to the painting, but the man in the art shop could tell me nothing beyond the fact that the work had been discovered several years previously at the house of a reclusive old woman on Charles Berrington Road in Wavertree.

One day I was gazing at the painting in the window, when an old man stopped beside me and stared intently at the same work of art. He complained that the sun would quickly fade the painting, and that it ought to be placed in the shady interior of the shop. I agreed, and the man started to reel off some amazing tales about the painting. He told me that the palmist in the scene was a Hungarian woman named Mary Strang. She had been paid a guinea by William Osbert to pose for the portrait. This is the rest of what the old man told me that afternoon on Bold Street:

Mary Strang's predictions were so accurate and uncanny, that the Church and the authorities soon banned her from reading fortunes in Sefton Park, where, in the summer, she would read the delicate palms of ladies out on their Sunday strolls. Mary was very swarthy, with long black hair, and her beautiful green

150

eyes were deep and penetrating. The gypsy had the reputation of being able to see deep into people's minds, and many avoided her because she could read their darkest desires and innermost secrets.

In the early 1890s, Mary upset a certain affluent Liverpool family by claiming that they were all cursed and would die terrible deaths because their ancestors had driven the poor people of Ireland out of their homes to die of starvation. Strangely enough, within a very short time, each member of the high class family that Mary had warned, started to die, one by one. The youngest died from scarlet fever, then his mother died soon after in a riding accident. The deaths continued until only the daughter was left, and she was placed in the care of relatives.

Black Mary, as Mary Strang was known, went on to make a very controversial accusation which ruffled the feathers of high class society. This took place one day on St George's Plateau in Lime Street, where Mary was selling artificial flowers, when she noticed a well dressed gentleman approaching the entrance to St George's Hall. Mary offered him an imitation carnation, upon which the man allegedly struck out with his walking cane and rapped Mary's hand quite sharply. She yelled out in pain, then, closing her eyes and concentrating very hard, accused the man of committing several serious and illegal sexual offences. The man, who happened to be Sir Leslie Stephen (brother of the celebrated Judge Stephen, who had sentenced Florence Maybrick to death at St George's Hall) turned purple with rage. Sir Leslie immediately fetched a policeman and had Mary thrown into the cells under St George's Hall, without a hearing, or even an official arrest, to teach her a lesson.

There may have been some truth in Mary Strang's accusations, because Sir Leslie Stephen should have reported the woman for defamation of character and slander, but he decided instead to use his connections at St George's Hall, and had her put in one of the darkest, coldest cells in the bowels of the hall. Sir Leslie probably only intended to confine the gypsy for a few days, but the woman became seriously ill, and died soon afterwards, but not before she uttered a chilling curse.

Judge Stephen and his younger brother heard through the grapevine that the gypsy had put a curse of death upon the judge. She had also claimed that Sir Leslie would be plagued by illness until his death. Shortly afterwards, and for the rest of his life, Sir Leslie began to complain of dizzy spells, which left him nauseous, but no doctor, even the most eminent in Harley Street, could diagnose the cause of his perplexing symptoms.

Just weeks after Mary Strang had cursed Judge Stephen, he died a slow agonising death, with a look of absolute terror on his face throughout his ordeal. For many hours on his deathbed he rambled on about the accursed Mary Strang, so many believed that the gypsy woman's deadly curse had truly come to pass.

Days after Black Mary's death, her ghost was seen roaming the cells of St George's Hall, and she even put in an appearance in the law courts. Many people who have worked at St George's Hall assure me that Mary's shade continues to haunt the place from time to time.

IGGY

One afternoon in 2006 I caught a hackney cab home from town, and during the course of the journey, the driver, a Broadgreen man named James Lamb, related a very strange story to me. At the age of two-and-a-half, James Lamb junior, the cabby's son, underwent a life-saving heart transplant operation at a hospital in Newcastle-upon-Tyne. The heart which young James received was from a German child who had died in a road traffic accident in Germany; that is all Mr Lamb knows about the donor who gave his son the gift of life. Little James made a steady recovery, but his father soon noticed intriguing aspects of the boy's behaviour which had not been evident before his operation. James often talked to someone invisible in the corner of the living room, and when his dad would ask the child who he was talking to, he would always say "Iggy".

As the child got older, his descriptions of the unseen Iggy became more and more detailed. James said Iggy was an 'army man', but naturally, his father surmised that this character was just one of those imaginary friends some children dream up – until Iggy was seen by two other people, that is. James Lamb senior says, "My two nephews stayed at the house one night, and they came running upstairs, both as white as a sheet and said there was a man dressed in uniform in the living room. They refuse to stay at the house now."

Not long afterwards, James senior was lying in bed when he heard a loud bang down in the living room. He thought a burglar was breaking in and ran downstairs wielding a baseball bat, ready to tackle the intruder, only to find that the noise had been made by a mirror which for some reason had fallen off the chimney breast and yet remained un-cracked. James recalls: "I said, 'Stop messing, Iggy!' and all of a sudden, there was an almighty crash in the kitchen. I was scared to go and see what had caused it, but finally I opened the kitchen door to find that a unit had come off the wall, and was now lying in the middle of the floor as if it had been placed there. Stranger still, that unit had been above the fishtank, yet it had somehow fallen without hitting the tank – as if the thing had defied gravity."

The mystery of Iggy deepened a few months later when Mr Lamb was carrying out a loft conversion at his home. He found an old brass-framed photograph featuring the faded face of a young clean-cut man. When Mr Lamb brought it downstairs, his young son saw it and said, "That's Iggy!" The hairs on the back of his father's neck stood on end when the child said those words.

The identity of the man in the picture is unknown. When I opened the back of the picture frame I found another photograph showing an unidentified elderly couple. So it looks like the mystery of just who Iggy really was will remain unresolved for the time being.

THE HITCH-HIKER

The following incident allegedly happened in Liverpool in 1979 and was even given a mention in a local TV news programme. In the autumn of 1979, a man named Frank Haines was driving his Ford Cortina along Queens Drive near Dunbabin Road in the Wavertree district of the city. The time was 1.45am, and it was raining heavily. Frank had been to visit his elderly mother in the Dingle and was on his way home. However, his Cortina had a troublesome engine and whenever Frank stopped at the lights, the car would be likely to stall or shudder.

On this particular, rainy night, the car pulled up at the traffic lights and the engine died. Frank had to turn the ignition key again and again to get the car to start. Seconds before he was about to move off, a girl came running through the torrential rain, waving at him through the rain-lashed windscreen. She ran up to the Cortina and tapped on the passenger window. Frank noticed that the girl looked as if she was about nineteen or twenty years of age. She wore a white rain-soaked tee shirt, a tartan scarf, and a pair of white flares. He leaned over and opened the door and the girl climbed into the car, slammed the door and sat in the seat wiping the rain from her face. She had long red hair and a pale freckled face.

"Could you give me a lift home, mate?" she asked, smiling at Frank.

"Do you always jump in strangers' cars like that?" said Frank, annoyed because the engine was refusing to start. As he turned the ignition key once more, the engine fired into life. "Where do you want a lift to?" he asked the girl.

"Barnham Drive, please," the girl replied and gave the number of her house.

"Where's that?" Frank asked, relieved that the car was moving along once again.

"It's off Childwall Valley Road," said the girl and she leaned back, let out a sigh and started singing a song that Frank had not heard for years. It was a Bay City Rollers song 'Bye Bye Baby'.

"What are you doing out at this time by yourself?" Frank asked the girl.

"I've been walking for the last half hour from Fir Lane through this rain. I hate the rain, don't you?" Then she asked, "What's your name?"

"Frank. What's yours?" Frank accelerated through a set of traffic lights that were about to turn red to avoid stalling again.

"Kelly."

"Well, Kelly, you'll have to direct me to Barnham Drive."

Frank drove to the Fiveways roundabout and carried on along Childwall Valley Road.

"Thanks for the lift, Frank. Are you going out your way for me?" said Kelly, beaming a smile at the driver.

"Nah, I'm not going out of the way; I live over in Court Hey. Now. Where do I go now?" said Frank, squinting at the road through the squeaking windscreen wipers.

"It's on your right here – no, its the next road on the right," said Kelly. Then she tapped Frank on his left leg.

"What?" said Frank, startled.

"Frank, could you do me a favour? But you'll think I'm really cheeky," said Kelly. "Could you wait outside the house for me, then give me a lift to my mate's in Chelwood Avenue? Could you?"

"Look, I'm not a bloody taxi driver. I'm dropping you off at your house and that's it," Frank retorted as he turned into Barnham Drive and stopped near the girl's house.

"Please, Frank. The girl touched Frank's knee and playfully pinched it, making him smile. "Pretty please?"

"Hurry up then. You've got five minutes. If this car doesn't start though, I'll have to walk home."

Frank shook his head. He wasn't usually the type to let himself be manipulated.

"Thanks, Frank. I won't be a minute. I'll just tell my Dad I'm staying over at my mate's."

Kelly left the car and dashed down the road in the pouring rain. She opened her gate and disappeared behind a hedge as she ran up the path towards the door.

Frank was thirty-three, but looked much younger. He wondered if he was too old to date Kelly. She only looked about twenty. He dismissed the thought from his mind and waited for her to come back. He waited … and waited. Fifteen minutes crawled by and Frank started to get annoyed. "That's it, girl; I'm going home," he muttered under his breath. He decided to just give Kelly another five minutes but the girl still did not return. Frank surmised that her father had told her she could not get into a car with a stranger. Frank started the car up first time and began to drive off but, a few seconds later, the car started to shake ominously and soon shuddered to a halt. Frank tried again and again to get it to restart but it just would not budge. He cursed Kelly and thought, "Damn it! She imposed on me, now I'll ask her for help."

Frank marched to Kelly's house and rang the bell. He knew deep down that it was also a good excuse to see Kelly again. She was a very pretty girl and Frank recalled with pleasure the way she had touched his leg in the car. A silhouette came and looked through the frosted glass. "Who is it?" said a voice behind the door.

"It's me, Frank. Is Kelly there?"

A bolt was drawn back behind the door and the handle turned. The front door opened and a man aged about sixty peered suspiciously out at Frank.

"Sorry to bother you. Is Kelly there?" Frank asked, dripping wet and burning with embarrassment.

"Kelly who?" the man demanded. It had not escaped Frank's notice that the man held an Alsatian dog by the collar with his other hand.

Frank described the red-haired girl he'd given a lift to and the colour seemed to drain from the man's face. He seemed flabbergasted.

The man explained that his daughter Kelly had been knocked down in a hit and run incident on Fir Lane four years ago. He was so shaken by the story, he invited Frank in out of the rain and showed him his photo album of Kelly. In one photograph, she was dressed in the tartan and white flares that Bay City Rollers fans wore and Frank remembered the song she had sung in his car – 'Bye Bye Baby'. Just before Kelly died, her friend in Court Hey had had an argument with her and cried her eyes out when she heard that Kelly had died. She kept saying that she just wished she could say she was sorry to Kelly.

It is said that Kelly's ghost still walks up Fir Lane from time to time and has even been seen by the police. In 1990, it was reported that a Royal Mail van had swerved to avoid the ghost of a red-haired girl who had then vanished in the middle of the road.

Two Terrifying Exorcisms

The following account was told to me by a Catholic priest who retired a few years ago. We were discussing the Rites of Exorcism, and he told me that even the holiest person is not immune to possession. True enough, it was recently claimed that Mother Theresa underwent exorcism shortly before her death. The priest said that the Church frowned upon the undue sensationalism which the media creates when reporting exorcisms, and it was only after retirement that he could take the risk of relating a couple of his truly amazing tales to me, without bringing down the wrath of the Church upon his head. I had never heard of this incident before, and after researching the claims of the priest, I believe it to be a true story.

In 1956, Ray, a thirteen-year-old Liverpool schoolboy, went to town with his Uncle John. Ray collected stamps, so his uncle took him to McGoff's in Moorfields, a shop that specialised in stamps and philately. John bought Ray a pack of assorted stamps and they left the shop. As they were leaving, John bumped into a friend he had not seen in years. His name was George Terry. The two men started chatting, and suddenly, Ray tugged on his uncle's sleeve.

"What is it, Ray?" asked John, annoyed by his nephew's rude interruption.

"Uncle, that man's going to die tonight," he said, indicating George with his eyes.

This naturally caused something of a stir and Ray was severely reprimanded and told to remain quiet when adults were having a conversation. His uncle apologised to his friend George, but later that night, John was drinking in his local – a pub called The Swan Vaults on Conway Street in Everton – when he heard some shocking news. That very evening, his friend, George Terry, after finishing eating his tea, had relaxed into his armchair, and had then died from natural causes. John thought about the morbid prediction his nephew had made earlier that day in Moorfields and he asked his nephew how he had known that George was about to die.

"I get this smell – a sweet sickly smell," explained Ray, quite matter-of-factly. "I think it's the smell of stuff they embalm bodies with, Uncle John."

On the following day, Ray's eldest sister, Janet, visited the family, bringing her little nine-month-old baby son with her. Ray asked if he could hold the baby, and Janet let him, but warned him to be very careful. Ray started rocking the baby in front of the fireplace, and suddenly, as the family was smiling and looking at him, the baby in his arms started babbling. Then it distinctly said: "Hello, Janet," and started to cry.

Everyone recoiled with surprise.

"Did you hear that?" gasped Janet.

"I did that!" said Ray, upon which his sister snatched the baby back, and everyone felt very uneasy.

It had not been ventriloquism; the baby had spoken clearly in a low voice.

On the Monday morning, Ray's mother entered his bedroom to get him up for school, when she came upon a horrible sight. Ray was lying on his bed in his pyjamas, and a thick, gooey, brown liquid was oozing out of his mouth and his eyes. It smelt utterly vile. Ray's mother frantically called her sister to the room and they used towels to wipe away the foul liquid, but it kept welling up in Ray's mouth and eyes and then his ears. They tried to wake him up, fearful that he might choke on the stuff, but he could not be roused. A doctor was called out, and he admitted that he was baffled by the brown, unidentifiable matter that had now swamped Ray and most of the bed.

Suddenly, the boy started to talk in a foreign language that the doctor recognised as Swahili. The doctor knew this because he had been raised in Kenya, where Swahili is spoken. Translating for the benefit of Ray's mother and aunt, he said that the schoolboy was muttering something about evil spirits. Naturally, Ray's mother was alarmed by the state of her child, and the doctor suggested calling a priest. As the family were Catholic, they sent for their local priest, Father Elliot.

The priest duly turned up, and witnessed a remarkable and frightening sight: the boy, now covered in the filthy, brown, viscous liquid, started to levitate slowly off the bed as he screamed out in terror. Father Elliot, Ray's mother and aunt and a neighbour, frantically tried to pull the boy back down on to the bed, but they were all almost lifted off their feet by the unseen powerful force that was making him float. The boy rose to the ceiling, where he left a dark stain from the revolting material issuing from his mouth. The powerful force that was gripping him suddenly released him and he plunged back down on to the mattress. Then suddenly, in a raspy voice, unlike his own, Ray began to speak.

"We're taking the woman at Number forty-nine to Hell!" he rasped.

Living at Number 49 in Ray's street was a Mrs Katie Walsh, and that very night she died of thrombosis in her sleep.

The priest decided to carry out the Rites of Exorcism on the boy using bell, book and candle, and he allegedly drove out five evil spirits, including the spirit of an Edwardian murderer. Ray returned to normality, and the priest visited him regularly for years, just to ensure that all was well. The boy was never possessed again.

The second exorcism which the elderly priest mentioned had been related to him by his uncle. Here are the unsettling events he disclosed:

In 1922, the father of a family of five living at the dwelling, was being haunted by a terrifying apparition. The priest was naturally sceptical at first, but he went along to the house in Aigburth and witnessed for himself the violent poltergeist activity. Knives flew out of a cutlery drawer and stabbed at the priest's palms, and on another occasion, hot lumps of glowing coal flew out of the fireplace, showering him and the family. An older priest soon arrived and advised the family to pack their bags and stay with relatives until the 'problem' could be sorted out. They followed his advice without question and went to stay with relatives up in Spellow Lane, Kirkdale. They were all so distraught that the local parish priest had to counsel them.

The supernatural activity in the house on Livingston Drive became more intense. Yellowish acrid vapours rose from the carpets, and grotesque leering faces appeared on the walls in the form of damp stains. An investigator from a psychical research society fled from the house after seeing a demonic head appear in the flames of the fire. The head spat out something deeply personal, only understood by the man, which affected him so severely that he never returned to the house.

In the cellar of the abandoned house, the floor would at times seem to give way, and the cries of tormented voices could be heard. Holy water was thrown down there in copious amounts, but it only seemed to provoke the chilling sound of hysterical laughter. A neighbour who once dared venture into the house to see what all the talk about ghosts was about, watched in horror as a massive, shiny, black beetle, about six inches long, came scrabbling after him down the hallway. He was so terrified that he flew out of the house in blind panic, and twisted his ankle on the front step.

Harry Price, a psychical researcher in London, also followed the case with interest when news of the inexplicable occurrences reached the capital.

An elderly nun who had dealt with visitations of the Devil, and was familiar with his crafty shenanigans, was asked to help. She left the convent in Hope Street and was driven to Livingston Drive. Clutched closely to her person, she carried her rosary, a Bible, and a silver crucifix. More importantly, she carried her faith, which was very strong, probably much stronger that the average cleric's. As the car was travelling at speed down Windsor Street, a swarm of hornets attacked the vehicle, and the driver had to veer off down Northumberland Street to escape the swarm. The nun suspected that the hornets were an obstacle from Satan sent to delay her. Then, as the old car was travelling up Park Road, the chassis started to shake violently, and the driver complained that something was wrong with the steering.

The nun ordered him to drive on and whispered a series of prayers; as she did so, the car gradually stopped vibrating. On Aigburth Road, a beautiful gleaming yellow Bentley screeched to a halt in front of their car. Two beautiful young ladies were in the Bentley, and the one who was driving sounded her horn and waved frantically at the driver of the nun's car. She was very attractive, and wore her hair in a stylish bob. The driver stopped the car and asked what the trouble was. He seemed entranced by the lady and her friend as they giggled and pointed to the bonnet of the Bentley. The nun left the vehicle and surveyed the ladies, who simply ignored her. The nun believed them to be another illusion of the Devil, conjured up to hinder and frustrate her attempts to reach the house on Livingston Drive. The nun urged the driver to take her to the house, but he seemed blissfully ignorant, because the two young ladies were taking off his jacket and telling him to fix the Bentley's engine.

The nun flagged down another vehicle and asked the driver to take her to Livingston Drive. He willingly agreed but, for some reason, he was unable to find the street. He had been reared in South Liverpool and knew the area well, but all of a sudden, he seemed confused, and he apologised to the nun. She left the car and found the house straight away.

What happened next is not too clear, but years later, one of the priests recalled that the nun had gone down into the cellar reciting, "Though I walk through the valley of the shadow of death, I will fear no evil, for thou art with me," and so on.

About five minutes later, an enormous, long, shadowy entity – about thirty feet in length, rose out of the cellar and passed through the top of the house. It had two bright points of light on it which looked like eyes, and it faded away as it drifted over towards the local park, before vanishing into the evening sky. The nun allegedly claimed that the 'thing' had been one of the ancient fallen angels which had been cast down on to the earth with Lucifer a long time ago. She felt that it had been awakened by someone in the neighbourhood who had been dabbling with the occult.

Not long afterwards, the man who had helped the two ladies in the Bentley said that just after the nun had left, they had completely ignored him and had driven off without saying another word.

THROUGH A GLASS DARKLY

Mirrors are the windows of the devil
Leon Garfield

The following tale of prophecy has been circulating the south end of Liverpool for years. There are several different versions and, although each variation of the story gives different character names, the name of Mrs Prentice is always amongst them ...

On the night of 14 April 1912, the *Titanic* struck an iceberg in the North Atlantic, on her maiden voyage and sank, with the loss of 1,513 lives. When news of the unprecedented maritime tragedy reached Liverpool, everybody, especially the relatives of those who had perished in the disaster, was saddened and very shocked. One person who was not shocked though, was Catherine Prentice, who lived in Upper Parliament Street, in the south end of the city.

Mrs Prentice, an elderly spinster, was regarded by her neighbours as something of an eccentric. She always dressed in out-of-date clothes from the late Victorian period and the curtains of her home were always tightly drawn. It was rumoured that she dabbled in the occult and some even suspected her of being a witch. One of her few friends was Mary Orme, an independent widow, who ran a local chandler's shop.

A few months before the *Titanic* made her doomed voyage, Mrs Orme told Mrs Prentice that her eldest daughter would be emigrating to the United States and would be making her passage on the luxurious White Star liner. When Mrs Prentice heard the name of the liner, her face became ashen and, in a broken voice, she warned Mrs Orme that her daughter Grace must cancel her voyage at once. Mrs Orme was naturally quite disturbed by her friend's entreaty and asked if she thought that something awful was going to happen to the liner.

Mrs Prentice foretold that the ship would sink after hitting an iceberg and that there would not be enough lifeboats to save all the passengers. Mrs Orme had long accepted that her friend had the gift of second sight and so took the chilling warning to heart. She pleaded with her daughter not to board the world's largest and most modern liner, but Grace was adamant that she would go and stubbornly refused to bend to her mother's request, saying that she was worrying unnecessarily. After all, it was a well-known fact that the *Titanic* had been described by her owners as unsinkable.

A fortnight before the doomed vessel was due to leave Southampton, Mrs Orme hid all Grace's savings from her as a last resort to thwart her planned voyage. This drastic measure had the required effect, but caused a bitter row to erupt between mother and daughter. However, when the appalling news of the great liner's sinking hit the headlines, Mrs Orme's daughter shuddered with relief and almost fainted from the shock.

In 1917, Mrs Prentice suffered a major stroke, which virtually robbed her of her powers of speech. Her condition later worsened to such an extent that she became bedridden. As she had no next of kin, she was tended by her only friend, Mrs Orme, and her daughter.

One night, Grace became tired of sitting at Mrs Prentice's bedside, as she seemed to be unconscious and she set off on a prying tour of the house. In an upstairs room she came across a crystal ball in the middle of a table which was covered in astrological charts of some kind. Fascinated, Grace tiptoed into the room and seated herself at the table and stared deep into the crystal ball. After a while, disappointed at seeing nothing, she grew bored and decided, instead, to have a browse through a bookcase of esoteric tomes of the occult, but soon found that they were too obtruse to be of any interest.

She was about to leave the room, when she noticed a reversed, oval-shaped picture hanging on one of the walls. Her curiosity was aroused and she turned the picture frame around. She soon discovered that it was not a picture at all, but a mirror. She gazed at her reflection for a moment, then saw a dark shape glide across the glass, making her visibly jump. Seconds later, the face of a man wearing a white tin hat appeared in the mirror. This apparition really frightened her and she stumbled backwards in alarm. The man's face in the mirror appeared to be talking but, although his mouth was moving, no sound was audible. Then the face vanished and a succession of other images appeared in the mirror. Suddenly, Grace saw something in the reflection which sent her fleeing from the house in a very distressed state.

When she arrived back home, crying and shaking, Mrs Orme immediately assumed that Mrs Prentice had died, until Grace told her about the ghostly faces she had seen in the bizarre mirror. Mrs Orme was stern-faced and angry at her daughter's prying behaviour and sharply told her that she should stop making such a fuss; she was simply overtired and imagining things.

Not long afterwards, Mrs Prentice passed away and, a couple of years after that, Mrs Orme and her daughter moved to Scotland Road, where they opened a small grocery shop. During the May Blitz of 1941, the two of them were sheltering in the cellar of the shop during an air-raid, when the building above them was demolished by a bomb, raining bricks and debris down on their heads.

After the 'All-clear' had sounded, Grace regained consciousness to find herself being pulled out of the rubble by a pair of strong hands. When she was back above ground and had wiped the thick dust from her eyes, she found that the hands belonged to an air-raid warden, who was smiling at her and asking if she was alright. She scrutinised his face which looked familiar to her. Then, to her horror, she realised that it was the same man in the white tin hat whom she had glimpsed in Mrs Prentices' mirror when she was a young woman. When she asked where her mother was, the warden slowly shook his head and told her that she had been crushed by a beam in the explosion and was dead.

Like many supernatural folklore tales I have heard, I took this yarn with a pinch of salt – until a couple of years ago, that is, when I read an intriguing manuscript in the main branch of the New York public library. The author was Bridget Hitler, the sister-in-law of the infamous German dictator.

In the manuscript, Bridget, an Irish woman who was married to Adolf Hitler's half brother, Alois, states that, in November 1912, twenty-three-year-old Adolf, at that time a down-and-out, turned up unexpectedly at Lime Street Station, where Bridget and Alois were expecting to meet Anton Roubel, a relative of Alois. But Adolf arrived in his place, admitting that he had made the journey in order to avoid being drafted into the German army. Alois and Bridget gave him refuge in their home at 102 Upper Stanhope Street in Liverpool's south end. At this time, the area was a magnet for German immigrants seeking work.

Young Adolf spent most of his time in Liverpool wandering around the city, particularly the Pier Head and, as he was something of a painter, he often visited the Walker Art Gallery. However, as time went by and he contributed nothing to the household, he soon wore out his welcome as a lodger and Alois accused him of being a work-shy layabout. When he had first arrived, Bridget had tried to teach the young Adolf to speak English but she very quickly tired of his superior attitude, so he was left to his own devices once more. There was one person recorded in the manuscript who got on extremely well with Adolf – a Mrs Prentice – who was said to be a neighbour of Bridget's.

Mrs Prentice is described as an astrologer, who gave tarot card readings to anyone interested in having their fortune told. Adolf was apparently fascinated by Mrs Prentice's talents and, in the manuscript, Bridget Hitler writes that, in her opinion, Mrs Prentice converted Adolf into an ardent believer in astrology.

JESUS AT LIME STREET

In the eyes of twelve-year-old Tommy O'Rourke, Jesus had arrived at Lime Street Station in a cloud of steam, with thunder rolling ominously in the heavens over Liverpool. This was on the Saturday morning of 7 July 1957, as rain hammered down on the great arched metal and glass roof of Lime Street Station. A man with dirty-blond shoulder length hair, with a Sacred Heart beard and moustache, emerged from the cloud of locomotive steam and smoke, carrying only a battered suitcase. He didn't wear a halo like the Messiah depicted in the oval pictures at his school, St Malachy's, yet Tommy still sensed that the man was very distinctive.

The biblical-looking man wore a modern dark blue suit. He strode down the platform, attracting sarcastic glances and bemused looks from the other train travellers as he passed them – long hair for men was frowned upon in the fifties. Tommy, however, didn't laugh at the stranger's appearance, he was transfixed by him.

"Excuse me, sir," said Tommy, catching him up.

The man halted, turned, then stared down at the boy with a pair of sad, brown and infinitely expressive eyes.

"Are you ...?" Tom's courage suddenly faded and he wasn't sure if he was asking a silly question. His voice trailed off.

After a pause, the tall man answered him in a well-spoken voice, "Who do you say I am?"

The boy's face flushed deeply and he looked down in embarrassment at the man's sandals.

"Out of the mouths of babes comes the truth. They will not accept me, but the eyes of a child behold me," said the man with a smile.

"Are you ... are you ... Jesus?" Tommy managed to stammer out the burning question.

"Thine own lips have said it," said the man with a gentle smile, just as two colourful Teddy boys, running to catch a train, brushed past him, swearing and laughing at his appearance.

"Get yer 'air cut, mate!" one of them bellowed.

"Judge not according to appearances!" shouted the bearded man, his voice resounding with some authority. He held the eye of the Teddy boy who had made the remark.

The Teddy boy responded to the challenging voice and stared back at the long haired gentleman, while quickly reaching into his pocket, perhaps to get his flick knife, but his friend dragged him away and on to the stationary train waiting at the platform.

Tommy was fascinated by the man who stood before him and the odd scenario he now found himself in. One minute he had been running to escape the rain by sheltering at the train station, wondering what to do with himself, the next minute here he was face to face with Jesus of Nazareth. He smirked to himself at the thought of the fantastic essay he could write about his school holidays when term started again at school.

Tommy decided to join the intriguing man as he walked away from the station and along Lime Street. The two figures walked on, shrouded by the mist of rain still falling, until they reached the Continental Café. In the man walked, with Tommy tagging close behind. He proceeded to order breakfast, and treated Tommy to an ice cream. When asked by a canny-looking Liverpool waitress whether he wanted extra toast, the man simply waved her away, quietly saying, "Man doth not live by bread alone."

The biblical quotation went straight over the waitress's head, and she chewed her gum and squinted at the man in puzzlement before wandering off to talk to a regular at another table.

A flutter of concern entered Tommy's thoughts. He knew that his parents had warned him not to trust in strangers, yet he felt incredibly safe with this man, almost instinctively, and had a sneaking suspicion that the figure before him really was Jesus.

The rain eventually gave way to pleasant sunshine and a stunning rainbow formed high in the sky, as Tommy and the man walked out of the café. As he had no fixed abode, the man made some enquiries about obtaining free shelter. Tommy stood behind the figure, simultaneously in awe and in fear, as his eyes fell upon the gathering of down-and-outs. He closely followed the man as he made his way over to the vagrants who were gathered outside on Lime Street, and politely asked their advice on where he could stay for the night. Most of the vagabonds replied with hostility, swearing at him and mocking his old fashioned appearance. There was just one tramp of a gentler nature named Anthony, who offered some help, because, he claimed through a drunken slur, that the modern-day Jesus had apparently driven devils out of his hysterical meths-drinking wife in the Legs of Man. Anthony politely, if a little hazily, directed the man he perceived to be an exorcist to the Vagrant's Hostel on Shaw Street.

After walking along a little further together towards the hostel, the man turned to Tommy.

"We must part here," he told Tommy, "for this is not the place for an innocent child. Go home, young man, and tell all you meet on the road that the Kingdom of God is at hand."

"Will you be alright with them?" asked Tommy, eyeing the assortment of rough-looking hobos sitting on the steps leading to a once fine Georgian House.

The man nodded, and placed his hand on Tommy's curly head.

"The innocent pure-hearted child is nearer to Heaven than the most devout Archbishop," he said softly, before entering the hostel.

Tommy felt a strange sadness at their parting, as he wandered off towards his home in the Dingle. On his way he passed his school, St Malachy's, and bumped into the school's priest, Father Keeley.

"Father!" Tommy shouted. The stout, rosey-cheeked priest turned to smile, then continued on his way. Tommy chased after him. Excitedly he told the priest all about how he'd met a man who said he was Jesus at Lime Street, and how he had driven evil spirits out of a woman in a pub. Father Keeley laughed at the young boy's imaginative story, before hurrying on his way.

Tommy's tale was met with a similar reception when he got home. His father, Dominic, warned his son not to follow tramps about, and his mother Christina reeled off a series of grisly tales of child murder, allegedly carried out by vagrants who had befriended children under false pretences. The only person who was open-minded enough to consider the possibility of Jesus being in Liverpool was Tommy's grandmother Patricia, known to her grandson as Nanny Pat. She listened carefully to Tommy's account of the long-haired man in a suit and sandals before relating an intriguing tale of her own.

"Years ago, a woman named Sadie used to mock our family because we were devout churchgoers, and she claimed Jesus had never existed and that the Bible was all made-up nonsense and all that. She worked behind the counter at the big Bon Marché store on Church Street." Her grandson was captivated, and Nanny Pat cleared her throat before continuing. "One day, a man came into the store and Sadie noticed he had the most beautiful pair of kind eyes she had ever seen, and he purchased the Holy Bible. She went to wrap it, but he held her hands and stopped her.

"It's yours, Sadie. Please take time to read it.'"

"I've heard this story that many times, I feel as if I was there in person," quipped Mr O'Rourke from behind his newspaper. His wife glared at him with steely blue eyes.

Nanny Pat continued her story. "Anyway, Sadie was taken aback a bit, because she wondered how the mysterious man knew her name. She handed the change to the man, and she saw that he had an open wound in the middle of his palm."

Tommy gasped as he realised what she was saying.

"Sadie felt the wound as she gave him his change, and saw that he had a wound in the other hand too."

"It was Our Lord," said Tommy, his wide eyes full of awe at the possibility.

"Next thing we know, Sadie's joining us for Holy Communion, all hunched up next to me at the altar rail."

Tommy was comforted by the story and felt deep down that there was a lot of truth to the day's incidents. He decided to say nothing more about the unusual man to his family, he was simply pleased that somebody had believed his surreal experience.

A week later, Tommy's grandmother became gravely ill. There was great concern and the family's doctor was called out. Tommy didn't hear what the diagnosis was, but was aware of the doctor speaking to his mother and father in hushed tones. His mother broke down in tears and was led into the kitchen by the doctor. Tommy knew things were not looking good when Father Keeley was sent for. The priest greeted Nanny Pat at her bedside and seemed pleased that she was wearing her rosary beads strung around her neck. She had a bottle of holy water on her bedside table. Tommy noticed that the words Father Keeley offered were far from positive. He seemed to be resigned to the old woman's fate. Tommy grew very conscious that he never once assured her that she would make a recovery. Tommy confronted Father Keeley and asked him to try and work a miracle on his grandmother. Once again the priest did not take the boy seriously and he merely patted Tommy's head.

"Jesus raised Lazarus, so why can't you, Father?" Tommy demanded.

Dominic was astounded at his son's audacity and seized him. He took him into the parlour to slap his legs.

Tommy was distressed and ran out of the house in tears. Desperate for help, he began to search for his friend at the Vagrant's Hostel on Shaw Street. Sure enough he found him preaching under the portico to the discards of humanity, and not one of them was laughing or sneering; they were hanging on to every word which the well-spoken spiritual man spoke. When the man spotted his young friend at the bottom of the steps, he curtailed the sermon and went down to meet him. Tommy told him all about his grandmother, who was seriously ill and not expected to live long, and the boy urged the drifter to come and make her better.

The man walked with Tommy to the house in the Dingle, and Mrs O'Rourke was shocked when her son introduced his long-haired friend. She barred his entrance at first, but Tommy started to cry, and begged his mother to admit him so he could save Nanny Pat. If Mr O'Rourke had been at home there would have been blood on the moon, but Tommy's father had just that moment left for work.

The man entered the lobby and Tommy took him up the stairs and straight to his grandmother's room. Nanny Pat looked pale, and made strange gurgling noises as she breathed. Tommy knelt at the bedside and whispered in her ear. He told her that Jesus was here now. He had come from Shaw Street, and was going to perform a miracle on her.

The old lady smiled, and then her eyes turned to look at the visitor.

"Patricia, arise from your sickbed in the name of Jesus. Come forth in the name of Christ!" the man commanded.

Nanny Pat sat up in the bed and began to cough. Tommy grabbed her handkerchief on her pillow and thrust it into her hand. The old woman was captivated by the stranger, and she was shaking slightly, or perhaps trembling in his presence.

Tommy remembered the tale his grandmother had told him about Christ visiting Bon Marché, and he slyly glanced at the man's palm. There was a scar in the centre of his hand! Tommy was now convinced that the man before him was telling the truth.

He asked how she was feeling.

"I just feel like some Guinness," she answered wryly.

Mrs O'Rourke was astounded at her mother's sudden return to health.

"Amen," said the man, and he turned to leave the bedroom.

Mrs O'Rourke could not believe her eyes. She hugged her mother, and asked her repeatedly how she felt. The old woman shrugged off the fuss and carefully made her way back downstairs to sit in her favourite armchair.

The man who had apparently affected this miraculous cure was halfway down the street, when Tommy's mother shouted after to him. She came running down the street desperately thanking him. She offered her hand, and as the miracle man reached out to shake it, she also noticed the curious wound on his palm. She saw no wound on his other palm.

"How can I repay you for my mother's health?" she asked.

The stranger just smiled.

"Love the Lord thy God with all of your heart," he said, before turning and leaving.

The doctor called at the house to confirm that Patricia had recovered but still needed some rest. Father Keeley learned of the incident when he also called at the house the next day. He was furious when he heard about the blasphemous confidence trickster who had supposedly cured Patricia with autosuggestion. He vowed to expose him as a fake, and that day sought advice from a senior priest.

A fortnight later, Patricia's friend next door, a seventy-nine-year-old woman named Daisy, fell ill. The outlook was not good and she was expected to die within days. The poor lady had been in and out of the Southern Hospital, but there was nothing the doctors could do for her, so they allowed her to return home to have her final days in familiar surroundings.

Tommy was certain that his new friend could help and told his grandmother so. She decided to listen. The two of them made their way to Shaw Street, but when they reached the Vagrant's Hostel, they found Father Keeley shouting at the man who had cured Tommy's grandmother. A circle of tramps surrounded the two men, and a corpulent, middle-aged policeman stood at the bottom of the steps. Father Keeley announced that he had reported the man "masquerading as Jesus", as he put it. Apparently the authorities were looking for a man matching the description of the mock Christ.

It became apparent that the unruly man's real name was Jeremy Fellowes. He was actually a thirty-three-year-old patient who had escaped from a mental hospital down south. He suffered from schizophrenia and religious mania, and had once tried to crucify himself, but only managed to nail one hand to a plank of wood.

The portly policeman next to Father Keeley stepped forward and grabbed Jeremy by the arm, then led him down the steps and away from the group of onlookers. Tommy and his grandmother rushed forward, and told Jeremy they needed his help. They tried to reason with the policeman, but he would not listen to their excuses.

Jeremy turned to Tommy and his grandmother. His eyes appeared heavy with sorrow.

"Tommy, I'm sorry," he murmured looking away sadly. The pained expression on his face told Tommy that he felt he had betrayed his confidence by leading him to believe he really was Jesus.

"I still believe in you," Tommy told him, his mind unswayed by the revelation.

Patricia stepped forward beside Tommy. She pleaded with Jeremy to try and help her dying friend, just as he had helped her.

"Come on, move along, missus," interrupted the policeman abruptly, his patience wearing thin. He attempted to push his captive towards the police station round the corner on Prescot Street when, suddenly, Jeremy managed to wriggle free and made a break for it. He took off down the street, with the out-of-shape policeman trying to give chase but instead ending up out of breath at the end of the street and clutching a stitch in his side.

That night, at precisely nine o'clock, there was a heavy knocking at the O'Rourkes' door. Tommy's mother was surprised to find on her doorstep the man who thought he was Jesus. She was reluctant to let the visitor through, but her mother Patricia invited the escapee in. She led him to the kitchen table and offered him some food and a cup of tea. She asked him earnestly if he would try and cure her friend next door. Jeremy smiled as he answered her and explained that her recovery had all been down to faith.

Despite Jeremy's reluctance, Patricia managed to persuade him to at least visit her sick friend. At ten o'clock that evening, Jeremy made his way into Daisy's bedroom. He was accompanied by Patricia who was so anxious she clutched his sleeve, and little Tommy was close behind. It was clear to all in the room that the woman lying in bed was very seriously ill. As Jeremy sat on the bed, he held on to the fragile lady's hand. Almost unresponsive, she just gazed into his sorrowful eyes with a faraway look.

Patricia was the first to break the intense silence pervading the room.

"It's Jesus, Daisy," she whispered, her tone comforting and calm.

At that moment the police hammered loudly at the front door. Daisy's son went to the door, annoyed that someone could create such a disturbance at the house of such a desperately ill woman. A detective accompanied by three policemen rushed in. It seemed that Father Keeley had alerted the police to the fact that Jeremy had gone into Daisy's home.

The detective stood in the doorway, looking into Daisy's bedroom. He beckoned Jeremy, and the wanted man reluctantly arose from the old woman's deathbed and walked to him with his head bowed.

"How dare you come barging in here when this woman is near to death," Patricia whispered to the detective.

"Help me!" groaned Daisy.

Jeremy turned, and moved a pace back towards the old lady. He knelt at her bedside, and held her hand tightly.

"Are you really Jesus?" Daisy asked him faintly.

Jeremy hesitated before replying. "Yes ... I am," he smiled.

"I'm so glad you came for me," said Daisy, her face noticeably eased by his words. The last vestiges of life were fading from her eyes.

"Daisy, this day thou shalt be with me in paradise," Jeremy whispered, with tears in his eyes.

The room was hushed as all eyes fell on Daisy, her face a picture of new found serenity. A vague smile remained on her delicate visage as all signs of life left her.

In what seemed like moments, Jeremy was escorted to the awaiting police car and taken away. Tommy stood close to his grandmother, overwhelmed by the experiences of the last few days. He hugged his grandmother and began to sob.

"There there," Nanny Pat said soothingly as she rubbed his back. Her wise eyes followed the police car as its headlights faded into the night.

TIMEWARP CHIPPY

Scientists, writers and philosophers have long pondered the elusive nature of time and space. Einstein was one of the first thinkers to suggest that time and space are interwoven, which means that you cannot look out into space without looking backwards into time. When you see the moon in the night sky, you are not seeing it as it is now, but as it was one and a quarter seconds ago, because it takes light one and a quarter seconds to travel the 239,000 miles from the lunar disk to our eyes. This time-space equation also applies to people and objects even closer to us. If you look at someone who is ten feet away, you are not seeing them as they are now, but as they were one hundred millionth of a second ago, because their light image takes that amount of time to reach your eyes. This short lesson alone hints that there is more to the nature of time and space than everyday commonsense would have us believe. The following fascinating event may seem unbelievable, but incidents like it are regularly reported and are usually filed under the inadequate heading of 'Timewarps'.

In November 1999, two students, Ben and Matthew, were returning from a Friday night out in the Varsity pub, which stands on Myrtle Street. The time was one o'clock in the morning. Both of them lived in the student flats on Mason Street in Edge Hill, so they decided to take the short, ten minute walk home. They set off up Oxford Street and passed the Oxford pub, where something strange took place. They saw a new fish and chip shop on the same side of the road as the Oxford pub, just past Florist Street. Neither of them had noticed the chippy before and thought it was strange for one to be open at ten past one in the morning. Strong neon lights blazed inside the eatery and the door was ajar allowing the appetising smell of fish and chips to waft past them, so they decided to venture inside.

The prices on the menu board were not written in decimal currency but in pounds, shillings and pence. The cash register was not electronic – it was the old mechanical variety, with large buttons like an oversized typewriter. One of the students tapped loudly on the counter with a coin, but there was no response from the back of the shop. No one came out to serve them. On one wall there hung a dated mirror with a ship on it and the decor was green ersatz marble.

175

When Ben turned around, ready to go back out, he was shocked to discover that the buildings outside the window were unfamiliar. Where a block of modern flats had stood before, there was now a huge dark building. Feeling very uneasy, the students walked out of the seemingly deserted chippy to find that the scenery outside had returned to normal once again.

At this point, Ben and Matthew felt an unsettling, tingling sensation in their limbs, as if they had walked through an electrostatic field and they noticed that their arms were covered in goosebumps. As they walked home, they kept gazing back at the place where they had visited the fish and chip shop, but there was nothing there but bushes and shrubs and it slowly dawned on them that they had visited a place which was not actually there.

I was particularly fascinated by the students' account because, just a few weeks previously, an ex-postman named David had asked me if there had ever been any sightings of the ghost chippy in Oxford Street. Apparently, quite a few people had seen it over the years. In a telephone conversation with me he urged me to get Billy Butler to ask the listeners if they knew of any chippy that once stood in Oxford Street near the Oxford pub. I took his advice and was soon overwhelmed with calls from listeners who had heard me relate the account of the time-displaced shop.

According to the majority of the people who telephoned in, a fish and chip shop had once stood in the precise location that Ben and Matthew had described. The shop had allegedly been run by a Mr Joe Coats (or Coates). People recalled that he had two daughters, Lilian and Joyce, the latter having been something of a figure-skating champion in her time. People had many fond memories of the fish and chip shop and remembered that Joe served delicious battered fish.

Why had a chippy, which had been demolished years before, suddenly reappeared that night, minus its staff? Your guess is as good as mine. I was so intrigued by the accounts, that I visited the site several times to conduct my own limited investigations, employing an experimental technique aimed at detecting anomalies in time. This involves the use of four highly accurate digital chronometers, all set simultaneously by a computer port. I placed the four chronometers in a square around the shrubs and bushes where the phantom shop had appeared. A few minutes later, bemused passers-by watched as I picked up the chronometers – and I noticed that two of them had lost one hundred and a fiftieth of a second. This test was repeated on the following day, when only one of the chronometers lost any time; a sixtieth of a second. This proved to me that time was running at different rates, in different areas of the site. In other words, a time anomaly exists near Florist Street.

I sent an e-mail to the physics department of Liverpool University, detailing the strange, disjointed time effect, but received no reply. I am used to being ignored by orthodox physicists, but I was still a little saddened. Imagine what the boffins in the university could do with the sophisticated hardware which they have at their disposal. For all we know, the frontier of time may be easier to venture into, than the frontier of space.

THE PEEPING TOM

The following story was investigated by a paranormal research group based in Hunts Cross and it concerns a creepy Peeping Tom who abuses his unusual psychic talent. Beware, because this sinister voyeur is still active! For centuries, mystics and occultists have claimed that each of us has a spirit-like entity, called the astral body, stowed away in our physical body. This astral body is said to contain the soul, the consciousness and the 'third eye'. It is thought that some people can project their astral body out of their physical body and view things which are happening miles away. Out-of-body experiences are also thought to take place when a person is in bad health, or near death. However, according to many yogis and mystics, we can all project ourselves out of our bodies with regular practice at meditation but it is thought to be a very dangerous exercise – there are reports of some people being unable to get back into their bodies after projecting from them.

If you think that all these claims about an astral body are bunkum, think again, because the CIA, FBI and several police forces in the United States and Europe have admitted that they are employing so-called, 'remote viewers' – experts who know how to project their consciousness out of their bodies so that they can view events taking place anywhere in the world. The CIA has admitted using remote viewers to spy on nuclear missile installations in the heart of the old Soviet Union and even NASA has admitted that they have employed remote viewers to see if they can find out data on other planets. Remote viewers have even been used successfully by police to locate the bodies of murder victims and missing people.

There is also said to be a remote viewer living in the Liverpool area who is allegedly abusing his psychic ability, in order to spy on women in their homes and workplaces. For legal reasons, he cannot be named, but paranormal investigators claim to know his identity. We'll call him Russell.

In August 1997, Josephine, who works for a chemists in the city, was enjoying a lunchtime meal at Wetherspoons, a large pub in Charlotte Row, when a small, middle-aged man, wearing yellow-tinted spectacles, came over and said, "Hi, Jo!"

Jo stopped eating and asked, "Who are you?"

"Russell," he replied, with a sinister sneer and he sat opposite at the table.

"I'm sorry, I don't know you," said Jo uneasily.

"I know you don't know me – but I know you," retorted Russell.

"What do you mean?" replied Jo, feeling intimidated by the stranger.

"I saw you cutting your toenails on your bed last night, just after you got out of the bath. You shouldn't use your fellah's razor to shave your legs, y'know. He has to use that razor himself."

"Are you some sort of pervert? I'm going to call the police now," Jo declared furiously.

"Calm down, Jo. Keep your hair on! You read too much Stephen King. You're up to page fifty-six of his latest book, aren't you? I visit you every night and you can't see me. I've even seen your little birthmark."

Russell described the exact location of the birthmark on a very private part of Jo's anatomy. Jo snapped and threw a butter knife at Russell. Then, as one of the staff came over to see what was going on, Russell ran out of the pub, laughing. Jo didn't know what to think. She wondered if Russell was watching her with binoculars, or a telescope, from the block of flats facing her home. Two years ago, Jo's friend had spotted a man in those flats looking at her with an enormous reflector telescope but Jo knew that a Peeping Tom with a telescope could not see into her bathroom, or behind the drawn curtains of her bedroom. She mentioned the creepy incident to her friends at work and they advised her to contact a group of paranormal investigators who had recently been featured on local radio.

The investigators told Jo that they knew of an eighteen-year-old girl in Liverpool who was also getting strange phonecalls and letters from a guy who said he could visit her in his astral body. The pest had said that his name was Russell. The research group said that they could not do anything about the psychic Peeping Tom and advised her to move to another area.

Jo convinced her boyfriend that she wanted to move to a flat near Sefton Park and he reluctantly agreed. However, the move made no difference; Jo was still under supernatural surveillance. A week later, she was in a shop in Bold Street when she felt a tap her on the shoulder. It was Russell.

Jo was dumbfounded as the stalker remarked, "Your other flat was better. The place you're in now is facing away from the park. Isn't that Mrs Davies a nosey old neighbour?" Russell added, "She puts a glass against the wall and listens to you and your fellah – especially when you two make love."

"That's it, I'm going to the police," snapped Jo. "There are cameras in this store taping you right now, so they'll know exactly what you look like."

Russell giggled.

"Hey, your fellah isn't very adventurous between the sheets, is he?"

At this Jo lost her cool completely and picking up a pan she whacked Russell over the head as hard as she could.

"You nutter!" he yelled as ran out the store.

At work the next day, Jo's friend, Lisa, confronted her.

"You're a real two-faced, gossiping, little backstabber, you are."

"What are you talking about?" asked Jo, totally baffled by this outburst.

"You know what I'm talking about," Lisa replied. "I got a phone call from this fellah last night and he said you and your fellah were slagging me off and saying I slept with three different men behind my boyfriend's back."

"Who told you this, Lisa?" asked Jo, her face turning crimson.

"Russell, this fellah who said he knows you," Lisa replied, taking a swipe at Jo.

A fight ensued and both girls ended up dragging each other around the shop by the hair, until a supervisor and a customer intervened.

When Jo returned home, she started to cry. She couldn't deny that she had said all those things about her friend Lisa and talked about her to her boyfriend but she had forgotten about the accursed eavesdropper, Russell.

Unfortunately, this story has no pleasant ending because Russell is, by all accounts, still roaming about the city and spying on women. So cover yourself up tonight and be careful what you say about your friends … because someone might be listening …

THE BOY IN THE RED TEE-SHIRT

HAUNTED LIVERPOOL 5

In November 1992, a twenty-seven-year-old woman named Lesley was abandoned by her partner of eight years. A selfish rogue, he deserted her and their seven-year-old son, Alan, and moved down to London, apparently wanting to make a fresh start.

Alan was an inquisitive young lad and he wanted to know the reasons behind his father's absence in great depth. His heartbroken mother tried to explain to him that his father had found another person whom he loved more than her, to which little Alan had responded by innocently asking why, and suggesting that his mother should tell him to come home and they would give him his favourite ice-cream. Lesley's heart burned with sorrow. How could she explain to Alan that his daddy would not be coming back?

She did the best she could to get on with what was left of her life. A dedicated single mother, she ensured that Alan never wanted for anything. The love that he had lost from his absent father was more than compensated for by his mother's constant affection.

Alan was a very hyperactive child and Lesley used to call him the 'little dynamo' because he was so full of energy. One day she returned from the shops carrying a red tee-shirt for him. She hugged him and joked:

"I was told to make you wear something red like a fire engine so people can see you coming. You move too fast."

Alan giggled and raced into the garden, imitating the sirens of a fire engine.

In 1993, Leslie took Alan to the doctor because of what she thought was a simple ear infection. She was shocked to hear the doctor ask her to take her son to see a specialist at the Royal Liverpool Teaching Hospital.

"But why?" Lesley asked, as a heavy ball of fear grew in the pit of her stomach.

"Don't worry," said the doctor, trying to allay her fears with a stock smile, "I just want a specialist to check on something, so we can be sure of ... er ... something."

Lesley took little Alan to the hospital and the specialist did discover something that absolutely devastated her: Alan had leukemia.

The spritely little dynamo gradually became too weak even to play. His health deteriorated over the months and Lesley was warned to expect the worst and prepare for the end. His last days were pure torture, although the neighbours helped a great deal, and Lesley's mother and sister did everything they could to ease his pain. One afternoon, Lesley asked to be alone with her son. She was holding Alan in her arms, gently rocking him, when the boy looked up at her and asked in a frail, strained voice, "Will I go to Heaven, Mummy?"

Lesley almost choked as she gave her reply.

"Of course, son," she whispered. "Of course, you will, love."

"Will you come to Heaven with me?" he asked, as tears began to stream down Lesley's face. She could only nod. Alan, though very weak, smiled when he saw this.

"When you get to Heaven, I'll have my red tee-shirt on, so you can see me straight away, Mum."

Alan gently turned to his mother and just managed a faint kiss, before passing away.

Naturally, it took Lesley years to recover from the loss of her beloved son. Her life carried on emptily, until August 1995, when she met a man named Mike. She soon realised that she had at last found her soulmate. Lesley had been so hurt by the experience of losing her son, that she decided not to tell Mike about him, preferring to wait instead until she was ready to open up and purge all the sorrow from inside her.

About a month later, Mike was involved in a serious car crash in Wrexham and had to be cut from the vehicle. When he awoke in hospital, Lesley was at his bedside, desperately clutching his hand. Mike appeared to be fine and after he had caught his breath he related a very strange and thought-provoking encounter.

He explained that while he had been unconscious, he had seen a little boy who was surrounded by a halo of golden light. The cherubine boy had seemed to be standing right in front of him. He wore shorts and had on a bright red, short-sleeved tee-shirt. Mike's faced softened as he described how the boy's face had been remarkably beautiful and radiant. The child had said only a few words, "Tell Mummy I love her", before leaving him.

When Lesley heard this, her eyes brimmed with tears of both pain and elation. She felt that she was ready to share her cherished memories of her late son with Mike and so a few days later she presented a picture of Alan to him.

"That's him!" Mike exclaimed, with a baffled look, as he held the child's picture close to his eyes and smiled.

The couple's bond was intensified by the inexplicable experience, and Lesley and Mike were later married before moving to Leeds. Little Alan remained central to both their lives.

GETTING INTO THE SPIRIT OF THINGS

HAUNTED LIVERPOOL 2

A lot of people, after having read my books, ask me how they can conduct superantural investigations of their own. I tell them that firstly, you need to find a location – haunted places where ghosts and other paranormal activity have been reported in the past. There are plenty of sites across the North West which are said to be haunted, although obviously, I cannot guarantee that a ghost will make an appearance at any particular time. Here is a selection which you may like to visit:

Speke Hall is well worth a look. For hundreds of years a white lady has been seen walking through the Tapestry Room. No one knows who she is, but she has been seen by hundreds of people over the years. Speke Hall is open Tuesday to Sunday and Bank Holiday Monday as well.

Chingle Hall, just north of Preston near Goosnargh, was built in 1258 from the wood of the Viking vessels that had sunk in the River Ribble. Chingle Hall was one of the last strongholds of the Catholic faith during the Reformation and many priests were killed there after being caught celebrating secret masses. The place has four secret passages where the priests once hid. It is said to be haunted by several ghosts, one of whom is renowned for giving visitors a friendly pat on the back, but the others are terrifying and have allegedly even attacked tourists. In one instance, a visitor felt an icy hand around his neck and was then flung across the room by an invisible force. A grotesque face has also been spotted, looking out of the windows of the hall.

St Oswald's Church. Each Sunday in St Oswald's Church in Ashton-in-Makerfield, you can see the Holy Hand: a small shrivelled hand encased in a glass casket, which is claimed to possess miraculous powers. It is said to be the hand of St Edmund Arrowsmith, who was martyred in 1628. The Holy Hand is said to have been curing people since 1736 and many pilgrims still visit the church simply to see it. The 372-year-old hand really is a most unusual spectacle. Over the years, in addition to the hand, many visitors to the church have also witnessed the ghost of an old highwayman, seen slowly wandering about in the graveyard.

Bidston Hill. Across the water at Bidston Hill, near Birkenhead, there is a flat, sandstone outcrop close to Bidston Conservatory, where you can see several mysterious carvings which are around a thousand years old. There are carvings of a moon goddess, with a cat's head, and a horse which exactly faces the midsummer sunrise. This area of Bidston Hill was venerated as a mystical gateway to another world in ancient times and many UFO researchers confirm that the area has an unusually high incidence of UFO sightings.

Caution for the Curious

The budding ghost hunter must remember that he or she is dabbling in a very serious subject. Investigating the paranormal should not be regarded as just another hobby like stamp-collecting, or bird-watching. Delving into an unknown phenomenon, which our present science cannot explain, requires a cool head and a genuine inquisitiveness, tempered with logic. There are many well-reported horror stories of frivolous individuals toying with ouija boards and later discovering that they have unleashed all sorts of negative malevolent forces upon themselves. The fate of such meddlers is often psychological illness. So, if you have no genuine interest in the supernatural sphere, beyond sensationalism, think again, because there is a very dark side to the subject.

To find a ghost to investigate is quite a simple matter. Statistically, quite a high percentage of the population (actually one in six, to be precise) has had a paranormal experience, so the number of people who know someone who has seen something strange makes it likely that you will often learn of a haunting through word-of-mouth contact. Three other good sources are the local press, regional television news programmes and the local radio bulletin. A browse through the local history section of a good bookshop will also be helpful.

Alternatively, you could join the Society of Psychical Research, who have extensive archives of hauntings all over the country and, in fact, the world. Once you have found the place where a ghost is reputed to haunt, you must adopt the same methods which the police use in a criminal enquiry. Record (by tape if possible) the description of the ghost given by any witnesses and take down basic details, such as the date, the exact place and time where the apparition was seen etc. If several people claim to have witnessed a ghost, interview them all separately and out of earshot of one another, to compare the described events.

Ask them what they were doing, or thinking, at the time of the sighting and even question them about their frame of mind before and after the occurrence. Also, take a careful look around the room or area where the ghost was seen and ask the witness or witnesses if they have noticed any objects which have been moved or damaged. Then, make a rough sketch of the place where the ghost stood and if it moved about, draw its route or trajectory.

If you are granted permission to lie in wait for the ghost on the premises, here is a list of some useful equipment:

Notebook and pens – for obvious reasons.

Camera – night-vision video cameras that were once only available to the military, are now routinely used by the public. A film camera may still have its uses in the ghost-hunters kit though. Digital cameras are very convenient to the person wanting to download images to the computer in a short time span, whereas 'analogue' cameras need to have their film developed, and this takes time (unless you're lucky enough to have your own darkroom). Digital cameras store the image in pixels, whereas SLR and even some disposable cameras, can capture the image in a state of higher definition on a suitably high-density grained film; and moreover, images captured by film cameras have virtually no orbs caused by dust particles. Orbs are to be seen on many images as transparent balls of light. Some are undoubtedly caused by dust and particles of moisture in the atmosphere, as well as lens flare, but a small percentage of orbs cannot be explained, and some researchers into the paranormal have interpreted these objects as evidence of spirits. In some cases, people have seen faces in the orbs, and there is a school of thought which regards the orb as the nucleus of a supernatural entity, which is usually invisible to the human eye when the picture is being taken.

Night-vision is of great benefit to the hunter of ghosts, and I have seen some spectacular footage of ghostly forms filmed with such cameras. When you're on a vigil with a night-vision camera, choose a good angle with some familiar object in your foreground (even if it's a gravestone), so it will give a good idea of how large or near the ghost is if it shows up. I have seen a lot of footage of lights in the middle of a dark background with no objects in the shot, and so it's difficult to say how far away the orb or ghostly image is and how big it is.

When using a digital camera for ghost hunting, I have found it's often a good idea to take a few photographs of the scene of the haunting, even when you can see nothing. The camera will often capture things your eyes didn't notice, even in broad daylight. Keep a notebook entry of each series of photographs you take, with the basic details of the location and the time the pictures were taken, as in the past, even I have lost track of where I took snaps and have had to do it all over again.

If you have long hair, tie it back or wear a hat, as I have seen so many so-called orbs that were nothing more than out-of-focus reflections of hair strands dangling in front of the camera lens.

If the weather is unusually cold, be careful you don't take photographs of your own exhaled breath; I have seen this done, and it creates a misleading ghostly effect on digital pictures.

Some people talk to ghosts they are hoping to capture with a digital camera or video. When it is quiet, they will say, "We know you are there, and we acknowledge you. May we take pictures of you?" You'd be surprised at the number of intriguing ghost photographs that have been produced when the researcher in the field does this.

Infra-red film – you may also like to experiment with infra-red film, which is sensitive to the invisible radiation at the end of the visible electromagnetic spectrum. But remember, because infra-red is a long-wave form of radiation, the focusing is different and you will need an infra-red filter. If in doubt, consult your camera manual, or any good photographic dealer.

If you don't fancy waiting around for the ghost to turn up, there are things called capacitance switches that can be attached to the camera. These devices will trigger the camera by electronically sensing the approach of a human or animal. Allegedly, they sometimes also react to ghosts.

If you have the resources and the ingenuity, you could set up a cine camera (with fast film), or a portable video camera and wire them to capacitance switches. Then there is the exciting possibility of capturing moving images of an apparition.

Tape recorder – for quality, use a reel-to-reel one if affordable, otherwise, the good old portable cassette recorder will do, loaded with a C120 low-noise cassette. An external microphone will produce better results than the recorder's built-in condenser mike, which has the annoying habit of picking up the noise produced by the electric motor of the tape itself.

Like the camera, the tape can be left to go off by itself, by either attaching a capacitance switch to it, or by attaching a pre-set electronic timer to the tape's REM socket. Alternatively, you can attach a darkness-activated switch to the tape via its REM socket. This will activate the tape recorder as soon as night falls, which is when things have a reputation for going bump!

If you can afford one, use a stereo tape recorder so that, upon playback, the direction the recorded noise originated from can be determined. If an ultrasonic transducer is plugged into the MIC socket, you may be able to record sounds outside the range of human hearing.

Thermometer – preferably a digital one, otherwise the old analogue type with a column of alcohol or mercury will do. Before, during and after any supernatural occurrence, take a note of the room temperature. A drop in temperature is a widely-reported indication of an impending materialisation.

Pressure pads – purchased from most electronic component stores, the pads, usually the size of a small mat, can activate a circuit when pressure is applied to them (for example standing on them) and are manufactured to be used in burglar alarms. A schematic circuit can be devised for an alarm that can be attached to a pressure mat. Pads will also indicate the presence of hoaxers!

Magnetic compass – this is useful to determine if there is any link with the appearance of a ghost and disruptions in the earth's magnetic field. For the dedicated investigator, a device called a magnetometer can accurately measure any magnetic anomaly.

Reel of cotton thread – stretch a thread of cotton across a room where a ghost is known to walk, to ascertain its solidity.

Watch – either an analogue watch with a luminous dial, or a digital one with a back-lit display. If possible, use a stopwatch to measure the exact duration of a paranormal occurrence.

Torch – a red piece of filter paper over the torch will help you consult your notebook or equipment in the dark without impairing your night vision.

Masking tape – this can be placed along the edges of doors and windows to prevent hoaxers moving into the area being observed.

Fluorescent powder – this can be scattered around the immediate area of the haunting. If any hoaxer sneaks across the area, the powder will glow on his or her shoes when illuminated by an ultra-violet lamp.

Also, researching the history of a haunted premises is essential, unless the ghost under investigation is the result of a recent death and has been positively identified by those people who knew the deceased, such as family and friends.

To dig up information on the history of a property the best place to start is the Central Library, where you can look up the address of the haunted house in the electoral register. This register, which was first compiled in 1832, is a list of all the people in the city who are entitled to vote. The register is published every year on 15 February and it gives the name and address of each elector.

Another good source of information is the church. For hundreds of years the church has been required to keep records of baptisms, marriages and burials. These records are usually written (sometimes in Latin) by the minister and his church warden. For instance, in the register of the Holy Trinity Church at Stratford there is an entry which reads, 'Gulielmus filius Johannes Shakspere' which, when translated means, 'William son of John Shakespeare'.

A basic knowledge of local history is obviously going to be an advantage to you if you are a budding ghost-hunter, so you should read as much on the subject as you can until you can mentally visualise what life was like in the different historical periods. Consult the old street maps of your local region and compare them with modern ones, also visit the local museum.

You should familiarise yourself with the different architectural periods. Pick an old house that you have seen and guess when it was built, then go and read up on it and see how close your guess was. Do the same with old furniture and other antique household objects. You do not have to study until you have the knowledge of an expert, just to the point where you can recognise the period to which an object belongs.

Besides camera equipment, there are other items the ghost hunter can carry in his kit to detect paranormal phenomena. *The Electro-Magnetic Field (EMF) meter* is about the size of a TV remote control unit, and it is employed to detect paranormal disturbances that generate electromagnetic fields. These devices usually filter out everyday mundane sources of electrical disturbances, such as mains frequencies and the interference of starter motors on fridges and neon lighting units. A similar type of device is a *Gauss Meter*, which will detect subtle changes in the earth's magnetic field which often take place when poltergeists and ghosts manifest. Sometimes, 'cold spots' have been associated with paranormal phenomena, and there is now an ingenious way to detect these zones of coldness with an *Infrared Laser Thermometer*. These devices usually have a pistol-grip, and you simply shine a laser beam at the places you wish to scan, and from a safe distance, a display screen on the device will give you a pinpoint accurate reading with a typical range of 0 degrees right up to 600 degrees Fahrenheit.

If you have access to the internet, simply type 'ghostbusting equipment' into the Google search-engine, and you will be able to see numerous websites detailing technical devices such as those I have mentioned. If you need to talk to like-minded people about ghosts and the paranormal, you can join my forum at www.slemen.com/forum and post a query about ghost-hunting or even show the results of any strange things you have captured with your digital camera to me and other members of the forum.

You don't always need computers and sophisticated electronic gizmos to hunt ghosts. Some people use good old-fashioned *dowsing rods*. Make your own simple set of L-shaped dowsing rods by getting two wire coat hangers and cutting off the long wires at the bottoms. Simply bend one end of each length of wire at about three to four inches from the end into a 90-degree L shape. The smaller end will be your handle and the long end is known as the pointer. Take a plastic straw or even use the case of a disposable biro and cut it in half. Place each of the pieces of pen case or straw over the handle end of each L-rod. This will be the sleeve of the handle and it will enable the L-rod to swivel freely without being affected by the muscles of the hand. Next, hold an L-shaped dowsing rod in each hand, pointing toward the object to be measured, and be sure the L-rod is horizontal to the ground. Now, hold the rods lightly in your hands with your elbows at your waist at a 90-degree angle. Your forearms should be parallel to the ground. Hold the rods straight out, parallel to the ground and parallel with each other. Don't place your thumbs over the bends in the rods, as it will severely restrict their movement. Also remember to hold the rod sleeves loosely and not to grip tightly. Walk towards the premises or site of the place you are investigating. Sometimes, if you walk over a grave, rods have been known to cross, and they will mysteriously uncross when you have passed over the grave. They will also sometimes react to a ghostly presence.

If you get results with a dowsing rod, you may also want to use a *pendulum*. Try to use a pendulum with a length of about 6 inches and keep the weight of the pendulum bob to about an ounce for the best results. You can make your own pendulum or buy one. People have used a simple cord or length of string with a crystal or charm at the end. Necklace chains have also been used. You must determine which way the pendulum must swing to indicate a 'yes' or 'no'. The pendulum will move in an elliptic, straight to and fro (or side to side) type movement, or in a circle. You may ask a spirit a question you know the answer to, and see what way the pendulum moves to represent the answer.

As ever, always take safety precautions when you are going to ghost hunt. If you're a minor, take someone older with you if you're going to a secluded spot, and always tell your parents or guardian where you will be, even if the hunt is in broad daylight. Carry a mobile phone with you if you possess one. Always respect private property when out on the hunt for ghosts, and be especially careful when investigating crumbling ruins, and dilapidated houses. Also be mindful of some ancient gravestones in the cemeteries of Liverpool, as there have been many tragic instances of loose stones toppling on top of people.

Now, with a level-head and a brave heart, go and seek the unknown and confront the mysterious society of spirits!

OTHER TITLES BY TOM SLEMEN

HAUNTED LIVERPOOL 1	Tom Slemen	£5.99
HAUNTED LIVERPOOL 2	Tom Slemen	£5.99
HAUNTED LIVERPOOL 3	Tom Slemen	£5.99
HAUNTED LIVERPOOL 4	Tom Slemen	£5.99
HAUNTED LIVERPOOL 5	Tom Slemen	£5.99
HAUNTED LIVERPOOL 6	Tom Slemen	£5.99
HAUNTED LIVERPOOL 7	Tom Slemen	£5.99
HAUNTED LIVERPOOL 8	Tom Slemen	£5.99
HAUNTED LIVERPOOL 9	Tom Slemen	£5.99
HAUNTED LIVERPOOL 10	Tom Slemen	£5.99
HAUNTED LIVERPOOL 11	Tom Slemen	£5.99
HAUNTED LIVERPOOL 12	Tom Slemen	£5.99
STRANGE LIVERPOOL	Tom Slemen	£5.99
HAUNTED WIRRAL	Tom Slemen	£5.99
LIVERPOOL GHOST WALK	Tom Slemen	£5.99
HAUNTED CHESHIRE	Tom Slemen	£5.99
WICKED LIVERPOOL	Tom Slemen	£5.99
HAUNTED LIVERPOOL, double cassette and audio book, read by Tom Slemen		£5.99

Available from all good bookshops
For a free stocklist contact
The Bluecoat Press
19 Rodney Street
Liverpool L1 9EF
Telephone 0151 707 2390

If you have had a paranormal encounter, or a supernatural experience of any sort,
please drop a line to Tom Slemen c/o the above address.